a
A PSYCHOANALYST'S NIGHTMARE:

These dreams

My dreams. .
Are neither **Freudian** *mengfutter* (German, "mixed fodder")
Nor are they egg foo **Jung**.
Ah, so –
no.
                                                                               It seems
such

dreams,
as I've recorded here, assessment to abash,
are mental landfill's pickins served as sheer conceptual HASH !!

([my comments concerning "actualities"/reality
appear as italics within brackets or parentheses.])

some of the dreams to come

The unconscious is a landfill into which our dreams spelunk to scavenge
Night terror or the vacuum's noise was mother's neural charges "heard"
My past life as a pigeon?
Submerged in the swarm of flies (like a fluid of amnion?)
Factories, tenements, alleys and corridors
Ruins and remnants, architectural and otherwise
Giant plastic head drains lake
Sacred bubble-wrap containing "holy air"
Organic monster fused with naval vessel in the other lane
The baby rhinoceros tied to the trunk of the car
"Dad, please don't keep putting ashes in my tea."
Baby seals kept as kittens until . . . brains sucked out . . . used as bait . .
Dogs in the gel-state between water and ice

Copyright 8/5/2012

ISBN 978 1300 86557 5

Appleton Schneider's dreams

I don't remember the first one.

So the second dream is the first I remember.
Earliest dream remembered? Looking out over a slanted edge of something I'm in (my baby carriage?) at stark upper levels of a row of 3-deckers. That almost imprint-scene has always brought me a vague sense of foreboding loneliness.

As for the third earliest dream . ..
And I'll never know if this was a dream or I was awake and experiencing what I think is called "night terror". From some sense of the room I was in, I must have been three? Four? Five? I both see (as if separate from) and feel myself lying in bed in that room, completely dark but for just slits of light coming through beneath and on the sides of a doorway. Living things seem to be in the room beyond the door. I seem to know they're my parents. But I'm alone in the dark and terrified. I'm saturated by sweat or the sense of immersion in other fluid. I try to call out but realize that I can't even breathe, let alone make sounds. And I'm paralyzed, can't move there in the dark. I hear a whining that seems to get louder and diminish in unpatterned variance. The sense of absolute helplessness and isolation is overwhelming even that of the panic that, not being able to breathe or cry out, I might never get out . . . of wherever I all but float . . . .
        [was I experiencing a flash-back of my gestation?, the whine of vacuum
        cleaner representing intrauterine sense of my mother's neural electricity?]

Next early dream.
Desert-like road on which I drive I see wrecked cars in gullies off to the side. Looking far ahead and up, I see a cave with a sort of balcony of rock in front of it.
[later, with my son, Jack, driving back from California, I see actuality very close to the dream's imagery.]

Next early dream.
In this dream, the narrow road I drive on alone continues into a distance that seems to end before what should be a perspective vanishing point. I sense this represents "unknown-ness". The locale I'm driving through seems to be at the vortex of steep hillsides rising on each side. There are small houses, each with a gable roof facing the road, a porch "underlining" their second story two windows. These little structures seem somewhat like desolate cottages or factory workers' houses. Some are side-by-side and close to the road. Others reached by drives, are back up onto the hillsides
   As I continue I feel foreboding and begin to notice that the houses seem vacant, abandoned, some windows broken, doors askew in their frames. On some of the

porches are partially destroyed furnishings, rubbish, globbish shapes on the floors. I want to hasten past even if it means more quickly reaching that invisible distance

I'm starting to feel actual panic and the images and configurations of everything become so vividly acute and sharp that they seem to lacerate my emotions through my optic nerves . . . until the searing surge of sight softens, becomes somewhat diffused, develops a sort of swirling kaleidoscopic haze that's conceptually comforting but only for a second because actual cognition comes and I realize that the swirling essence now encompassing me "atmosphere" is . . . . is . . . flies. At first they seem a "fabric" of appearance but then closer the congeal to be seen clearly as swirling billions getting even thicker as I find I can't slow down my vector into the swarm and soon I am immersed and can no longer see nor breathe nor cry out . . . even to the vacant and the desecrated little structure-hovels, themselves now disappearing in the flies and sense of suffocating buzz . . . .

> *[I must have been in my mid- teens for this intriguing dream, of horror-helplessnes. And was it a case of late-stage night-terror, recapitulation of "gestational experience" (fly swarm as amniotic fluid?) . . . or was the dream a premonition . . . . . ?]*

And the next. It may have been the next night or the next week. The proximity, if not temporal definitely associative, connected this second dream with the "realm of the flies". In this (seaquel?) I seemed to be driving through the same place as before, but no longer a vortice. Rather, the land on both sides of the road just sloped gently upward. The cottages on each side were less clearly seen other than that I knew they were there and that they related to (or were extensions of) those in the former dream. There was no semblance or sense of the previous ruin, abandonment, desecration. I drove on, in this dream remembering the flies and being relieved that they were no longer of concern. I emerged from the cottage realm as if leaving a subdivision.

Then this one.
Racing along what appears like a NYC avenue (but no traffic) and for some reason it seems I'm in (or I am) a taxi. Accelerating, I fly past cross-streets, not having to stop. But then I'm rising from the surface of a street that's like Tremont or Washington – in the Roxbury area of Boston. I'm then flying under the elevated train structure until I land to perch upon a girder.

> *[memory of a past-life as a pigeon?]*

And . . .
Seems like I'm on a trip South (I think I actually dreamt this when we were heading to SC and staying at a motel in NJ. This was very early in marriage. Dreamt I was in a playground beside a building and there was a sense of anxiety. No people present, but the cause of my feelings I somehow knew relate to the people in my marriage, my wife and her three kids. I next seemed to have passed all the way through the building and come out the other side where I felt comfortable, all situations resolved.

> *[On waking, I had the immediate realization of not just marital/kid problems – but also a sense of "coming-through" regarding sexuality – to a "place" of content and stability.]*

Another.

My father in a wheelchair coming out of an ocean's heavy surf. He's advising me, finger pointing, that I must cut down on smoking.
[Didn't accomplish anything until about 25 years later!!]

Another

On a twisting highway through all kinds of industrial regions but up into hilly, rural places. Night. Lost? Just touring? I see no one and arrive nowhere. At least one other time I had this same dream.

I'm on a desolate stretch of road, it seems walking. Suddenly I become aware of a elongated structure set back from the road and up on the side of a hill. It seems to be brick or stone, and even from a distance the massive expanse is obviously abandoned. With foreboding I head up the overgrown drive toward the place. Closer, I clearly see that the central part is four and five stories in height, and above its facades peaked roofs and pinnacles arise with little dormer-like windows.

Out to each side from this central cluster, first three, then two-story wings extend several hundred feet as continuous structure, but angled every hundred feet or so as if a zig-zag. One familiar with the massive mental institutions of the 1800s (Kirkbride design) can easily picture what I see in the dream.

Close, I approach the gaping entry under its collapsing peaked roof. I feel afraid. afraid to go in.

Suddenly I'm in and surrounded by a realm of ruin rising above me into invisibility except for the strands and sheets and shards of this or that which are hanging loose from above and off the walls around. The effect is that of being in a cave where the stalactites have become fragments of walls and woodwork and their descent is drawn by a gravity of omni-directional chaos.

At this point my fear has become terror as I look into the diminishing distance of one of the corridors off into a wing. At first there's ambient light as I step carefully between objects on the floor. On one side, through openings whose doors are smashed or hanging from only one hinge, vague illumination mixed with haze and webs of dust or spiders seems like an infection. Through shattered windows from the outside slivers of sunlight stab the embolic interior light so that it seems to seep into the corridor and toward me. I move along past that room and another and on toward the eventual disappearance into black's oblivion of any features.

But prior to that infinity I come to where the floor deteriorates, rotted, collapsed, cascaded somewhat as if a dry stream bed where architectural parts of stone and wood strew. I can only see that this descent is as if into something bottomless beneath the ruins.

Now, dreaming the scenario and that I'm also consciously experiencing the dream-terror, I take the first step downward into the unknown.

Another.

At first I'm looking down as if from a plane coming in for a landing and passing at low altitude over a slum area. But then I'm on the ground within the tenements, whose facades, as if semi-demolished Victorian and Queen Anne and Gothic mansions, were now two-dimensional, flat, but configured with pinnacles and dormers and brackets and columns and more embellishment. But this all seems to represent a kind of architectural decay, I realize. This is not the Bronx with substantive brick and stone. It's framed facades, reduced to a kind of mere fabric through which not only ragged window and door apertures are openings. There are wounds penetrating the surfaces which have no more actual substance as architecture than do paper cut-out-dresses-or-such have for past-age little girls' paper dolls. And in the dream I wonder if I'm just a paper doll dressing myself in ideas and ambitions that will never be of substance.

[It seemed that I returned to this slum area several times in subsequent dreams. But it could be that it was only in one dream that I dreamt that I had dreamt that I had dreamt the imagery before]

It seems like a passageway enclosed in heavy iron beams and plates. On one side slits of daylight come through and I realize that I'm swimming against the violent flow of water within what should be the track bed and surroundings of an elevated rapid transit train. I have a ticket clenched in my teeth and, despite the surge against me, I'm making headway. I realize that behind me (unseen but assumed to be high and dry) there's a class of grade-school children for whom I'm responsible.

Another night and I'm in the same channel of water, but swimming with the raging flow. I reach a point where the single sluice divides and distributes and disseminates into myriad directions and outflows and creeks and brooks and fibrils, suggesting something arterial and organic, but also, and also in my dream's assessment, suggesting somehow the outflow delta of a major river.

A barren, flat landscape stretches ahead and on each side as if everything had been demolished to clear-cut ground level, leaving hints of what might have been a mall on one side and even an airport on the other. I approach a crossroad where a plow must have heaped up a berm of snow across my road. On one corner of this intersection there are gray, distorted and decayed rectangular shapes suggesting remains of what had been buildings. I drive ahead, across the berm, on into the indiscernible bleakness of a three-dimensional vanishing point except for its incremental effects: desolation, desperation, desecration . . . as I dream. I come to a delineation and realize that beyond this suggestion of cessation of surface, from the infinity of one side to that of the other, there is nothing ahead. For I have reached a precipice that borders a nadir.

A street upon which I drive past tenements on a hillside to my right. On the left the land slopes down where a rubbish dump is slowly filling up a seaside marsh. The trash, dumped in piles, is set afire each night and as I turn down the road into this inferno the flames are high above and soon all around me. I drive on in between the clumps of flaring and fuming mass and seem to be heading right into an immense spread of consumption ahead and seem not to care at all.

The above were quite vividly remembered early dreams through the many years. No doubt I dreamt innumerable more of which any awakening image or emotion was just "subducted" back into the unconscious magma.

For some reason, starting last year my dream dynamic became such that it almost seemed that I was awake and imagining dreaming what I was actually just dreaming!! And on awakening, the vividness of what I'd dreamt was such that I started taking notes. As dreams continued and notes accumulated, I entered them into this file. And as the file became substantial, it seemed like a good idea to format the content and get it published.

At this point in time and date, the extent and extremes of my dreams made me realize that in not keeping a record, I was wasting a veritable "resource" of my mind's creativity (or lunacy . . . .)

So . . . starting just below, the "contemporary chaos-conceptuality" of my nights' mental meanders.

**A confounding collection
of contemporary dreams**

Sunday, 10/8/12

Rockport-like sea-side scenery. Driving by men laying up granite pieces in a walls surrounding perhaps a tiny, single-family cemetary. Pieces of white granite are set like petals of flowes or cactus rising from ground.

Next, some room with table, Aaron, from work, I there too. I have my manuscripts and all over table, also a countertop. I start to remove them to put into a vehicle in lot outside.

Rooms somewhat like in a 3-decker, but also with hint of Linden Square buildings (before bank). Wall heater throwing out heat *[heater on floor in trailer room where I'm sleeping]*. Electricity goes out and I'm outside talking with people regarding possibility of short circuit.

First it seems I've gone through either mall or foyer of some kind of gallery (amusement/games?). But then seems to be the basement area of the Bear Hill Golf Club. Waiting for someone who's in restroom, I walk past cafeteria-like area and reach signs for hot cornbread (which look like round pies in kitchen area in background behind counter). I'm going to get some, but then I'm told each piece is $18. Immediately I'm with a large group of other people protesting the exorbitance. I've apparently trespassed into the place, but I state loudly that "we're members of an elite country club" and something to the effect of " . . .this is a fucking insult . . . "

Then, it seems I'm in Rockport again . . and in a cemetery beside the wall, beautiful views here or there of the sea which it borders. I seem to be with Bonnie. Although we aren't engaged in anything sexual (actually no visuals of her), there's an element of turn-on for me, but not with her. That she's married is part of my disinterest in her as focus of my dream-arousal.

Then I've come upon a young couple with a baby in a carriage and a toddler-girl to whom the mother (an appearance of a young Laura) is trying to explain something about an oven – but then it's regarding something the kid (or wind?) has constantly been slapping against some siding resulting in almost a botanical image-transfer (like a stain or impression) from the object onto the wall.

[I awake, look at clock (1:15), it seems having been quite motivated to start (with this one) recording my dreams while still asleep and dreaming it. Take leak, turn on desktop, and jot this down until 1:30.]

10/9/12

Driving through hilly streets with old houses – then through a lower area beside a stone wall – then on a narrow highway's breakdown lane with a large camper vehicle in front of me that I can't pass, so drop behind further. Next I'm transferring stuff from one car to another. Then Dale *[a driver at work]* and I are supposed to go somewhere for some kind of tests. Uncle Billy is giving direction that we should go straight down 93. But we only have one glass of milk and no trailer to take with us. I say, we'll have to go in my car.

Next, in a warehouse with ramps down and up. Wait for a pallet jack to go past and on toward a furnace beyond, but at that point it's a dead end. So I'm walking toward a parked FedX truck and then trying to hide some equipment in front of it.

10/10/12

Rearranging boxes of books etc., but leaving room for toys or balls.

Diana and I discussing "sexually suffused faces and genitalia".

Got my Mack tractor back from repair and for first time go to new terminal and park in the yard by garage doors. Find it's gone (dispatcher Ron sent it to CA). I set out in car to retrieve it from road. Stopped along the way, I look out window and see penguins waddling by.

10/11/12

A casino or hotel foyer-like area, furniture being moved in, tall, very effeminate manager (?) of the place in dispute about whether something is a personal problem or policy change. He requests the number to call the Bureau of Indian Affairs.

In a cluttered shop with jury rigged tools of all kinds. The guy who owns it is a lawyer and asks if he can list me as a reference or if I'll be responsible for something (for him). I tell him yes, but I'm only home on weekends.

On foot on steep hill behind parked trucks and then walking chest-deep through loose snow

10/12/12

Booth-like building, not a phone booth, but there's a phone in it. Beyond, there seems to be a party going on, teenage boys and girls, one of the latter looks like Josephine Woods *[a girl friend way back]*. She wants to stay over.

Next I'm talking on the phone with her father, who then appears along with a group of extremely freakish-looking people amid the partiers.

He allows that she can stay over and party with me and the scene now seems to be in the hall of an old Masonic building, quite decrepit. She announces she's leaving.

I'm next talking in the foyer of an office building, my tractor-trailer rig idling (in the foyer) and inching backwards into a jackknife. But then it's moving forward and into a corridor and I can't catch it to stop it.

10/13/12

A little girl kind of beneath a table. Audience in background. She's reaching up and touching things on the table and saying, "torn earth, torn earth". Somehow this seems to have something to do with dental cavities.

By the ocean next and a sailboat passes almost too fast considering the wind.

Oldsmobile with aunt Marj. Should get rid of the car. It's wearing out and has body damage, but someone (me?) is saying that she likely won't..

George *[my job's terminal manager]* is in a huge conversion bus. He wants me to play piano for some military event. I say $250.

Outside on a phone and telling (niece) Patsy to call me later .. as a huge daddy-long-legs is seen.

In Volkswagen with Rich and Bonnie and trying to find a gas station. We approach a beach down a kind of "sand-sluice" embankment, but then have turned and gone back up, gone right, and in and out of a bar, warehouse, and refrigerated locker in a huge cold-storage warehouse.

Next, alone in a busy small-city square. It's late at night? Midwest or N.H. All gas stations are closed, I'm told.

Bunch of kids in a dumpster in a cellar. I go upstairs through a party scene, people with noise-makers and hats and party napkins in front of them on a long table set in a corridor. Outside, another table and a girl is licking lipstick off a paper. I approach her and see portable radios on her table, with trip-wires attached and stretching across the path I'll have to tread.

10/14/12

I've called on the phone but then I'm in San Diego and Laura's on the floor looking for dirt. But suddenly I'm in the office of Gilfoy *[a building supply distributor]* and Peter *[the owner]* has wakened me from a sound sleep and he's throwing me out.

Riding a bike (unseen location) but suddenly I'm seeing a Chinese guy climbing up the quoins on the corner of a brick building.

It seems to be an International Harvester Co. executive I next see. His wife is commenting about his trying to impress higher-ups. I tell her "he's just a local operator-pal in the big business leagues".

10/15/12

A long warehouse that borders a river (or harbor) is being torn down. Inside, still intact, is a corridor with a hung ceiling. Somehow I realize that above it is the original arched ceiling, several feet higher. "Appleton" and
"Schneider and other names once designated the occupants of the warehouse. For some reason the whole dream relates to the Presidential debates.

10/16/12

A hillside of rocks and concrete debris, some scattered out onto a wide, paved lot. I see what seems to be a woman taking picking up pieces and filling in depressed areas of the lot beyond, and she's next using pillows as well as rocks and concrete shards.

Next a segment in a living room with furniture rearranged and someone doesn't like it because it leaves space on one wall.

10/18/12   An amazing dream I remembered dreaming – but not its content!!

10/19/12

Square, very deep shaft (like rectilinear missile silo). I descend into it but can't get into any of the industrial spaces off platforms.

Next into people's house and they're complaining of having a large rat that has built a nest in their ceiling light fixture and they can't get rid of it. It seems Nick (very little here) is with me. They say he can sleep over, but a phone call comes that Angie's been taken to the hospital.

Walking with Rich and Angie along the high embankment of an abandoned rail line until we reach where a trestle had been across a gully. Angie stays above (it seems, behind, no longer in the dream-sequence).

At a tourist-like plaza around somewhat European village-scene buildings. In one is an alcove with a marble-slab as a urinal. I pee. Beyond this alcove a corridor stretches into another men's room area, then beyond where it seems there are arcade games, pinball machines, etc. People are passing behind me even as I pee.

Outside again, with Bobby Martin *[one of the drivers at work]* and Nick (?) or Josh (?), now grown-up, whichever of the latter worried that if he doesn't get somewhere to pick up his pay check it will be forfeited because there is no "roll-over" for non-picked-up checks. But he can't go get it because Angie is gone.

Last scene along a gravelly beach and I'm saying (regarding Angie), "She could be a real bitch, but I miss her" . . . and in the dream (and on awakening) there seemed to be a sense/insinuation that I would join her . . . . .

10/20/12

2-story office park with numerous separate buildings, all of which have had their exterior walls removed. Thus the inside room partitions etc. make the buildings appear like stacks of shipping containers (or those large household moving modules).

Some kind of business being run from a street-side, dumpy little warehouse but with a loading dock. They have an old fashioned-style pallet-jack-forklift combination device with which they're unloading something from my car (or truck). Something's mentioned about cutting Joistape and they say, no problem, and one of the guys goes to look something up in some catalog . while another is lifting a loose stack of furniture with the jack. He's trying to place it atop another stack of furniture, the arms of chairs on the bottom pile serving as "racks" on which to set the upper.

Then I'm watching dogs first cross a divided highway, then mainly focusing on one starting to race along one lane and somewhat morphing into a vehicle – from his head backward, his body becoming like a car's hood, and his genitals, penis pointing, becoming positioned thereon like the hood ornament of a classic l930s Packard or LaSalle or such.

10/23/12

In the dream I'm being asked (or I'm asking) whether "The Week" (a publication equivalent to Time or Newsweek) is printed weekly or daily. But then there's some kind of contest or at least comparison of shopping carts. One is mine, the other some unknown person's. In each are all kinds of personal and technical and mechanical items. The challenge is to be chosen as the neater of the two.

10/24/12

Again, as in a previous dream, I'm in what seems like a partially demolished building. Down a shaft I see that there are children living in a dumpster and making a lot of noise. As I walk toward the outside, I pass a wheelbarrow in which charcoal is burning so that people can cook their cheeseburgers. Next there are tables along a walkway. At one a girl, not seen to be the one from previous dream, sits and is licking lipstick off a paper.

Suddenly I seem to be in the fusion of a truck repair facility and an operating room. I sense that I'm with professionals who, along with me, are watching the circulation of something fluid through transparent tubing (or arteries – because somehow I know this is a cardiovascular arrangement. The tubing/artery is shaped like an arch, fluid rising from bottom left, up over the apogee, and down. Between the "legs" of the arch is a cross-tube (picture a printed capital H with the lines above the horizontal bending to touch each other). When we see that the fluid is not only flowing up and over, but also through the cross-tube, we're satisfied that it works.

10/25/12

Looking to rent an apartment. Seems to be Lawrence, MA region, for I am on a wide street that resembles a main one in Lawr. But then it's a side street with 3-deckers that have been restored. On one, the mortar in the brick joints hasn't been tooled and I find the slumping effect interesting. But on another, because there hasn't been mortar tucked between the brick and the windows, someone has absolutely globbed black tar.

Inside and upstairs in a building. A woman somewhat resembling Martha Radditz *(the moderator of the VP debate)* is showing me the place. Pass thru a common room full of old people, on and into a room where an old man has lived but either moved out, or died. Someone is saying what a comedian he was, always telling people he had Mae West in there with him – and some believed him.

The apartment is beautiful, newly renovated. I'm going to take it. For it seems that the whole building (a 3-family) is priced at $6,000. New
carpet, paint, etc., but outside the door to the unit I'm going to live in there's
years of paint and dirt and Walter *(one of the drivers from work)* is showing me how he'd spent weeks grinding it down to a clean surface.

Now it's Howie Feingold *(a friend from way back)* with me. The real estate woman is telling me there's a problem with my buying the place. The seller (seems to be something to do with the City) wants more money. It seems that I'm much younger than I am – for in thinking over what could happen if I moved in, I realize I could be screwed in the future – even thrown out from what's supposed to be elderly housing.

Suddenly I tell the woman I won't go thru with it. I get my deposit back.
Same dream, next scenario . . .
Driving tractor-trailer rig and I'm in an industrial area resembling Chelsea. Pull to side where my delivery is to be made and I notice too late that beside the pavement, an area has been grass-seeded. Someone had already run over it, and the receiver of my freight isn't upset that I have too. Just tire marks on the dirt – no damage.

As I'm walking to the back to the trailer, the trailer starts to tip over toward me, but I manage to upright it. Then it's tipping toward the other side, but the guy gets it upright.

I'm in the trailer to bring the freight to the tail when I notice that the whole rear half of the trailer, from halfway up, has been sprung (as if something very heavy was dropped on the roof, the rear span of which is gone as if scraped away. What remains of the upper sides is bowed-out, the ribs mangled.

Back at the terminal building it seems I'm showing the terminal manager and eliciting practically no response from him.

10/27/12

I'm in a long commercial corridor. On one wall is a wide window looking out onto a crowd of people in front of whom is a very hairy man (his shirt is open) sitting at a table, looking into the window. Suddenly he convulses in agony and the crowd surges forward to help him, for one of his legs has been severed by something.

The next scene involves a murder that's been committed and for some reason his extreme fascination and curiosity about the case has resulted in one of the detectives being targeted as the prime suspect

10/28/12

A steep hillside. Overhead, power lines. Above on the slope, a structure that resembles either a Buddhist monastery of Tibet, for example – or a ramshackle office building. I'm standing with someone else underneath one of the steel towers that hold up the power lines. Elsewhere on the hillside there are numerous people who seem to be a gathered there for some kind of promotional event or presentation.

A bit up the incline, a couple of young, very pretty women stand, dressed in saris. One of them has a bull horn and she's addressing the attendees. One of her messages is to suggest that they go up to the building and see the originator of the business-at-hand *(mortgages? – I'd been reading a book on the sub-prime debacle before going to sleep)*.

My unseen companion and I are next right in front of the building, being told that the person we wish to see is busy at the moment, and we should wait.

10/29/12

A woman named Golda is coming down rock steps into an area where she's stopping at "stations of the cross". At each she recites, "I peed here, I squeezed here" while someone shakes a branch over her head. A small crowd is following and observing reverently.

Joshua Bell *(a famous classical violinist who became even more famous by anonymously playing violin in a NY subway station)* is in the middle of a field (football?). There are bleachers beyond where he's playing prodigiously on a piano!! In my dream I'm rather amused and astounded that, as well as his talent, I'm noticing his Jewishness.

Next there are Jewish Catholics at a gathering somewhere in Boston between something owned by Schlumberger *(oil drilling equipment corporation)* and the IRA. Whatever the event, there are sparse people in a room with peeling trim paint and wallpaper, the effect being that of a terribly neglected, weathered, tenement interior. The wallpaper is a dull, but vivid blue (and this is the first time I ever really dreamed color!!!!)

The last segment has something to do with a child wanting to go to a movie, but his parents insist on going to Europe instead and as he frets, his father appears dressed only in a jock strap.

10/30/12

A huge, concrete (floor, walls, ceiling) almost empty factory or warehouse space where I first find Nick's *(my 24 yr old grandson)* office *(in reality his occupation has nothing to do with an office – except maybe that of his boss)*.

Next I find myself in an even more vast empty industrial space where I just stand and wait for him to finish his shift (it seems the previous empty space has become some kind of production facility where he works. As I wait I watch a tiny kitten frolicking around on the floor.

Out on the street I find myself. I intend to fart but produce a large turd in my pants. A nearby Panera Bread store has a rest room I use and with no problem clean what hasn't made any mess at all.

Next I'm witnessing a crowd of people protesting to preserve language that's being taught in "Facebook-ese" ("2 bad, CU latr " . . . etc.)

Then I'm beside what, in my dream, I find myself thinking "a regiment of vans" (parked light delivery trucks) as a crowd of people marches by. Overhead, clouds race along (and in the dream I'm actually phrasing the description) "like fragments of ice swept along in river-rapids".

11/1/12

I'm looking for some place off Arsenal Street in Watertown, MA. It's where you'd be if you karate-chopped the map—and it would then lead you to where you could sell gold as you head West.

Next I'm showing someone a proposed picture through my camera's viewer, and as we look at the building I'm trying to figure out if it's the one in front of us. But then I'm explaining the camera's view of an old, unused railroad line stretching off in the distance – and that I've been taking a series of pictures of abandoned railroad equipment and routes.

11/3/12

I'm first on an upper floor of an old factory building (the interior somewhat resembling scene from the movie The Pajama Game. It seems I've been hired for whatever is being done in the place. No people appear, but I must have completed everything, for I find myself descending the narrow, winding stairs *(resembling stairway in actual Lawrence, MA warehouse, on one of the floor of which "Fruit Slices" candy is made}*.

Next I'm driving into a two-level parking lot, through the lower, up into the upper. On I drive through very narrow street *(vague resemblance to part of Winthrop, MA., also the North End of Boston)*.

I'm now inside a consignment shop, occupying what must have been a one story factory (or large store) space. I look at carved pieces of this or that, some carved marble (and a couple I recognize as fragments of birds that once adorned the head of some saint statue somewhere). There's a black, Lionel-like steam locomotive model (on its side) among other toy trains on a counter.

Downstairs in the basement area I'm approached by the one of the owners (this, the husband), and told that what he hasn't sold of what I'd placed with him has been there for over two months.

I agree to remove items, explaining that I have to get to a new job, so can't take all at once. I grab an upright vacuum cleaner and am looking for something else to take back. He and I mention my new job, its preferable location (in Everett, MA), and that I'll still be staying in the parking lot during the week. I'm enthused. He's skeptical.

On the way through the first floor the wife hugs me and tells me they've sold their condo and are moving. With her is a young Hispanic helper who taps me on the shoulder and says (regarding frugality) that Angie and I have always been an inspiration to him in his life's struggles. At first I didn't quite get what he was saying, and kind of disregarded him, but realizing, I explain that I don't hear too well, so it took me a minute for what he'd said "to come through".

Now it's getting late and I'm due at my new job before long. Into the parking lot, my car not to be seen. Lower level, no car. Back up. Maybe I drove it into the narrow streets and parked? Walking through the street (now resembling Rockport, MA with little shops along one side). No car. The street has suddenly become a narrow corridor within a vast apartment complex. Carrying the vacuum, I find it difficult to walk quickly along due to the tiny corridor.

I'm in a young woman's apartment, explaining my predicament, now getting desperate because I'll be late on my first day of new job. She's opened a sliding closet door for me to look in. I'm back (with her) in the corridor which comes to an abrupt end. But the closing wall is actually just thin Styrofoam panels which slide up (top part) or down in tracks. I can just barely climb over the lower and get outside the corridor, it seems back into a narrow street.

Still sensing horror that I may be fired before I've even started my first day, I contemplate that I should have stayed at New England Motor Freight, where almost no matter what, I'd have been job-secure.

(Starting before I awoke (it seemed) but continuing after until even now (20 min. later) I wondered whether this dream was a drastically impressionistic contemplation of the approaching end of my life. The "new job", an unknown and at present unreachable destination (can't find the vehicle). But I've gathered loose ends (the vacuum from the consignment place, and made arrangements otherwise).

11/5/12

First part. I'm in some sort of mental health facility with buildings set in a woodsy area. I'm specifically inside an office where, for some reason, I'm telling a psychologist (or counselor) that she has no right to act like Ronald Reagan is her father. A little boy patient in the room with me *(who resembles my niece's son in reality)* has the appearance that Ronald Reagan would have as a young boy. The kid is at the facility due to some form of brain dysfunction *(which, in actuality, my niece's son has minimally – and Reagan eventually did devastatingly due to old age dementia).*

Next I'm at an airport and parking my tractor-trailer rig on the tarmac in order to make a delivery. Something concerning a separate tank on the truck is for chemicals to scrub exhaust gas of particulates and catalyze gaseous emissions to neutrality. *(this relates to the reality of emissions control on commercial vehicles).*

Next I'm on Kathleen Drive in Franklin, approaching #17 where the front lawn *(in front of where the shed was)* seems to be a vastly broader spread of lush grass with a brand new stretch of garrison fence between the house and property line. But as I progress I see that the front lawn is scraggly, and on towards Marie's house *(on the other side of #17)* the side yard is an immense stretch of overgrown, unkempt reforestation. As I look back at that side of the house I see that it's sided with vertical boards, and stretches back to the extent of an office park building.

11/8/12

Although it's in a stairwell, the scene bears a resemblance to the set of the sit-com "Cheers". A counter/bar separates me from people inside the barrier. One of them who looks a bit like Ted Danson *(the owner of "Cheers")* has asked what I've read lately. To my reply, *Les Tres Quartorz* he states he's read it and it's bland.

I'm coughing a bit, and a woman seated inside the counter/bar, who is smoking, mentions my cough and first offers me some kind of pill. Her voice is almost masculinely low, husky. Next she's gone to the other side of the area and come back with a cigarette for me.

Now into another realm which seems to be an outbuilding of some food-prep industry. Various pieces of stainless steel equipment are here and there, but my focus is along the base of the front concrete wall where there's a continuum of device (which closely resembles over-sized baseboard heating. I've been removing cellophane here and there and finding, within the unit, refrigerated lettuce, packets of meat, and other stuff. I decide I should re-cover all and leave it alone.

Now going up a staircase with someone else. We're both carrying a long tube *(bringing to mind an actual long package I delivered during my day's work).* The tube seems to be some kind of super-weapon or gun, for when we arrive at a large upstairs room I jokingly announce "BOOM" and startle the others.

There's some kind of extremely complex electronic device that I assume has to do with espionage or communications. As I sit at a table, my partner leaves. An unknown woman approaches the device which is on another table. She sits down, unnoticing my noticing her, and begins manipulating the controls of the device. . . . . . which, I somehow realize, is inter-connected with the towering (maybe 20' tall) sculpture in a totally different room, realm, perhaps even country!! A woman with sculpting tools (such as one would use working with clay) is working on a lower portion of the figure. Suddenly from within, above, there's a sort of little landslide of partially congealed clay that pours out and down, and on this "tide" is a craft resembling a Viking boat. I realize that this is the result of the woman at the machine in the other area of the dream.

Now a corridor that both resembles a corridor to which I delivered gift boxes several times many years ago. But there's also something about the locale suggesting the porch of some grand historic summer-resort hotel.

At any rate, Lynn (one of the clerks from work) is there as I climb a set of stairs to the corridor level. She's advising me about something having to do with continuing work as opposed to retiring.

11/10/12

In a room with unrecognized people. Someone has brought in a huge cat, dark red (though actual color not seen) with black, blotchy spots. It stares at me, its ears raising and lowering, articulated like bat wings. It rubs against me, almost knocking me over.

Next in a conference room which narrows to be more like a corridor with a sofa in it. I'm sitting beside some sleazy, salesman-like guy who has a prospectus for the boat that Paul (my son-in-law), someone else, and I are going to invest in. Now, just beside the corridor (which has become like a pier), a boat operated by Paul is moving away from us, making the consummation of the deal appear unlikely. So the guy and I are standing and, perhaps, about to leave when a large rat appears which the guy picks up and hands to me. We quickly take it to a rear egress from the corridor. At the foot of stairs up to ground level, the rat ravenously starts chewing on part of a banana.

The guy has disappeared, but now I'm at the top of the stairs from where the rat/banana were. Beyond, the ground slopes downward to a sort of containment pond surrounded by industrial buildings. I approach the edge of the water and on the other side (someone points out) there's a truck, colors very much like New England Motor Freight. It's moving through the water, likely to get stuck, but doesn't.

Back on the upper ground level I'm walking back toward the stairwell down (where the rat was).

Next I'm inside a room whose décor I've designed and built. On each side of a four-poster bed are three very ornate columns, fluted, affixed with plaster appliqués, composite capitols, the lower third or so boxed-in.

Lace curtains drape the left trio, beside which is a drop of heavy velvet. On the incomplete right trio, I need to do something for completion but can't.

Seemingly a continuum from the column-room is a vast, desecrated interior space where all kinds of tools and hardware and hoses and compressor and more are strewn, stacked, etc. I'm looking for what I need (nails, something else) to complete work on an area where I next find myself. . . clinging to a narrow, rotted beam four stories above the ground on the back of this building. I have to nail the last of loose boards. I drop the nail. A little girl somehow beside me hands me a screw which I manage to use as a nail. Off to one side, between the rafters I see a tool box, stretch to reach it, but it's heavy and I can't move it. Almost wailing in fright, I lower myself to the ground.

And I've followed a hose from the tool-strew area. It runs perhaps several miles through apartment areas of the city and its end is down in a catch basin. For some reason I needed to find that end of the hose to turn on a spigot to get water out of the other end. But now I find that it has to be the other end that would be the source of water, for this end has to fitting to go onto a faucet – and, being in a catch basin, no faucet.

Almost simultaneously with waking (it seems) the big red cat beginning of the dream-sequence (?) again became cognitive focus (though not any image at this point) Figure all that out!!!!

11/12/12

Elite area of houses, a couple here or there joined together giving the effect of an immense mansion from the front. But from the rear the properties are obviously commercial/industrial buildings with large truck-dock doors. In the dream I wonder how the builders or owners get away with such dual zoning.

Next I'm in a hardware store considering whether to buy a heavy duty ¾ inch drill. The price has been lowered from $60 to $26. The salesman wants me to buy bits too, but I realize that I have (in actuality) a sufficient number of drill bits, some of which I'll never again use.

I leave the store, apparently heading for Chris's (my daughter) but in a valley area through which I drive and look up at the backs of houses on ridges overhead on each side.

11/13/12

Driving something across a wide median strip between highway lanes. I start to bog down in deep, loose sand – which then turns to snow. I shift into all wheel drive and am able to progress. (During the day I'd read an ad for a Range Rover with 3-option drive train depending on sand, snow, or pavement)

11/14/12

At a lawyer's regarding a will or trust revision. Joshua Latham is not seen, but his uncle appears (who retired from the firm, Joshua taking his place).The uncle, David Latham, in the dream appears to be the same age (30s) as Joshua.

11/15/12

(This I wrote while apparently still half asleep) . . Using the Wilmington iron worker, Joquith Heath, was a stroke of genius to demonstrate that the male inventive superiority of a "flexible urinal" really pertains to the source of the urine rather than its container thereafter. Between the parked trucks whose mirrors were mutually cleared when doors were opened, he relieved his needs easily, flexing his faucet in whatever desired direction.

11/16/12

Riding in what seems like a school bus. There are a few children in the other seats. Outside, the view is over fields as we ascend a hill. Atop, the school bus has become a corridor within a building, one of several that seem like some kind of institutional cluster separated by walks. But inside, where the bus seats are still on either side of the corridor, there are still the children. One, a kind of chubby little girl of perhaps 2 or 3, comes up to me, presses her cheek against mine, and whispers, "My name is Murial".

11/17/12

I arrive with tractor-trailer rig (53' trailer) at an old industrial area which bears some resemblance to Clinton, MA *(but also a building that seems to have something to do with Callahan Electroplating in Malden, MA)*.

I pull into the yard of some industrial business. I'll have to back out. There are decrepit cars and other "stuff" in the area. I exit the truck and go looking for someone, finally finding out that they won't be able to unload me for a couple hours *(which relates to an actual delivery situation of the day before)*. I call dispatch and am told to wait.

Returning from where I'd made the call, I find the truck is gone.

And in the next sequence of the dream someone else and I are walking through hilly streets of old 2-family houses (some with rubbish out font for collection). We're searching for the truck but don't see it. A cop in a cruiser pulls slowly out of a driveway and I wave to try to stop him, but he either doesn't see me or doesn't care and just drives on down the hill.

Then I'm in a combination major construction site (huge excavated pit where piles and foundation forms are) and parking lot, kind of adjacent to the pit and almost like a "configuration mirror" (square at ground-level and same size as excavation). As I walk along with a bunch of other people (it seems I'm looking here for the truck), patriotic music starts playing and people are reciting the pledge of allegiance. I find there are tears streaming down my face as I join them, but my voice only a whisper of the words.

I'm next in the parking place (next to the pit) and crossing it while someone is talking about how terrible African-Americans are as hockey players.

Last scene is inside a warehouse just about stuffed with merchandise in disarray and worse. A lot of it seems to be insulation material, loose from rolls, leaking from bags. Beyond me and further within the mess, someone on a forklift realizes my presence. He seems to be telling me that he's got something to do with unloading my truck so that I can eventually get on with the rest of my day's work.

11/22/12

I've parked my pickup truck on a street in an area resembling the Longwood Ave. hospital complex. And I next find myself standing at a counter in a lobby that could be of Children's Hospital (or Peter Bent). A guy is looking for Angel Street. We peruse some hospital pamphlets but don't find any kind of map or directory. I drop a couple pages of something which he picks up. I thank him.

Outside, I look for my vehicle but can't find it. In this dream I realize that in prior dreams I've also dreamed of not being able to find my vehicle (both a personal vehicle and, at least a couple times, a tractor-trailer rig). As I search and experience anxiety (has it been towed?), I see an antique auto go by – it seems to consist of two front halves fastened together (so that on each end there is a hood).

I'm next in a yard, the house unseen but I've exited it and crossed the somewhat bare (no lawn) yard to where a gigantic tree has fallen. Its trunk is as long and straight as the tallest ship's mast before any branches. Someone else and I are commenting about inadequate root structure. I explain that with this type of tree, very little root is necessary. The tree is next suddenly standing straight and, as if it were but a long weed, I pick it up. Revealed is one spindly sprout of root.

11/24/12

An early run for the trucking company. I'm bobtailing in some city or other. Narrow residential street with other tractors parked (one a sleeper with someone moving within it). I park and walk a few houses down to where there's an entrance to the parking lot of a mall. In the mall I enter a Sears to buy cigarettes.

Leave the Sears and as I walk back out of the lot I notice young people, some dressed far too lightly for the cold temperatures.

On the street. My tractor is gone. I go way up the street, way down. No tractor.

Next I'm on a bicycle still looking for the tractor. Down a long grade and up into a dirt road off the paved one. I come to a dead end, which is the yard of a colonial-era house. The yard and shrubs and stairs are absolutely strewn with dungarees.

I retreat out onto the street and through another low-lying area which seems to be park and playground on both sides of the street. I come to a small building and lean the bike against an outside counter, enter, and I'm in an area used as the administration office for the playground and park.

On one side there's a man relating something about hearing someone tell some person that English has become the default language of the world. My first inspiration is to mention Esperanto *(an attempted "universal language" back in the early 1900s)*. But I suddenly realize, and say, that "mathematics is now the ultimate universal language *(in the dream, flashing through my mind are such factors as variant languages, scripts, pronunciations, musical notations, etc. – but numbers are numbers throughout the world).*

The guy gets up to leave, commenting that he agrees with me. The woman to whom he was talking now focuses on me, listening as I tell her that I have lost my truck. I inquire what town or city I'm in. I'm told it's Milton, MA – a rather yuppie realm, and I almost make a comment (relating to the guy and the English-as-Esperanto comment) comparing Milton to Concord, MA.

I'm getting desperate because it's getting late and I need to locate my truck to get to work. I ask for the phone number of the police (maybe the truck was towed?). Suddenly the woman is writing-out a list of groceries that she wants me to pick up for her.

(It seems that prior to waking, still in the dream, I'm aware that I'm dreaming. Also that I've had similar dreams (of being lost or not being able to find a vehicle). But since it's just a dream I don't need to be concerned with getting to work because it's a long weekend and I'm actually at home, in bed, and dreaming!!!! Before the need to pee actually wakes me, I dream (in at least two repetitions) that I'm at the computer and recording the dream).

11/25/12

I'm driving the tractor-trailer rig, leave the highway and continue over fields and sections of dirt road and through valleys and finally come through the back side into a large parking lot, apparently behind some kind of industrial or commercial buildings. After a phone call to dispatch, someone from the building comes out to meet me. I'm directed to back up to an area where others start to unload, box-by-box, the full contents of the trailer.

Then it seems as if I've gone directly from that scenario to enter the back door of an old, somewhat Victorian residence which has been converted to a nursing home. Someone named Brad has just been admitted and I have some kind of connection or relationship with him. That's why I'm there.

I sort of wander through some of the public areas, not crowded but there are quite a few people, staff and others. The place is run-down but not dirty, the furnishings threadbare and worn, but everything seems clean.

Then I'm sitting in a large office area. Two women are there with me, at least one of them apparently a psychologist on the staff. We're talking about Brad's development of an interest in some kind of video game which involves dexterity (demolishing target things, from cliffs to buildings). The woman is concerned that his fixation on manipulation may interfere with his (it seems)
recovery of linguistic function.

I state that manual and linguistic behaviors (and neurology) are of different brain domains, so his video-game activity should be something quite apart from any neural interface with language. But . . . that by a therapeutic interface (first the counselor describing what Brad's doing, and ongoing Brad himself putting in language his intentions (in the video game) and also his accomplishment (step by step – or in summation-retrospect) . . . . there might actually be achieved a reciprocal reinforcement of dexterity and linguistics.

The women appear impressed with my statement.

I take my leave of them and go out into the public area, looking to find Brad in order to spend some time with him.

11/27/12

It seems I'm inside a stadium's seating area. Tiered concrete arcs are seen on downward into murk. Apparently the structure is being demolished. There are no seats. There's debris all around. I'm wheeling some kind of freight on a hand truck. I tip the load off the hand truck against the remains of an upright girder.

Next, inside a framed colonial building (like an old tavern or something) with hand hewn beams evident as the supporting structure. It seems that a builder and architect come in and I ask what to do about the suspended ceiling that had been installed at some time. The rest of the chamber is truly antique integrity. I'm telling the two men that I'd read of (or that I myself had installed in a restoration job) a replacement ceiling. This was arched and consisted of tongue and groove boards, somewhat free-from secure fastening to the arches of the frame-support. Thus, the weight of the boards would compress and minimize the seams between them.

And still in the same dream, I'm with a woman on a very narrow, shrub and tree encroached street. Something about her living off this street, about freight, about her husband being disabled, that she was going to have to move. *[I wonder if all these fragments relate to my job (freight), the woman next door in the trailer park whose husband had a stroke, thus she might have to move, the street from somewhere I'd driven years ago].* I continue on and emerge from the narrow street into what looks like Exeter, NH. *(where my cousin Jeanne had lived).* Now I'm driving a 53' trailer and in order to turn around and head back, I have to go up over part of a church lawn.

And then I'm at the back of a truck trailer with some young woman. We're trying to pry up the metal plate on the trailer floor by using a forklift blade. It just barely gets under the plate but slips loose before really picking it up. Some kind of wedge needs to be slipped under as the fork presses against and raises up the plate. I warn the woman not to put her fingers under the plate as she pushes a wedge while I raise the fork and thus, finally, the plate. Next she and I and others are upstairs in a building. I enter a bathroom with three toilets, no stall-separations. I'm about to defecate in one when the girl comes into the room. Then another, neither seeming concerned that I'm shitting before them. I feel a bit uncomfortable.

11/28/12

Looking down from a low-flying airplane. Below seems to be Mission Hill *(part of Boston).* Back Bay stretches off into the distance, hazy, indistinct. But the top of Mission Hill is occupied by a commercial development constructed of concentric circles of highly colorful materials and lit brightly by multicolor lights as well. *[The configuration and coloration – not really seen as color in the dream, though "known" to be colors is that of a picture of a painting done by a student at BU's school of art. Picture was in recent alumnus magazine I read].*

12/1/12

Watching TV news broadcast which is showing the main playroom of a shut-down child-care facility. A number of puppies are provided to be the kids' companions and playmates (neither kids nor dogs are seen in the dream). The floor of the large room is littered with dog shit.

Next, up into a building and in a tiny lobby where a counter and glass door separate the visitor from the inside space. The place is a Marilyn Munroe museum. Stretching almost to a vanishing point beyond the door inward is a corridor. On each wall are pictures. It seems that there are myriad rooms on either side of the corridor, all dedicated to displaying Marilyn memorabilia.
I'm saying to Angie that we'd better get inside and started on the tour. We kind of sneak around the counter and open the glass door.

Then I'm with a physician, it seems a cardiologist. He and I have been talking about our respective occupations. I've stated that at least I have time to to read, to learn – being a truck driver. He acknowledges that, and also that his role allows almost no time (in fact not enough time) for him to sufficiently interact with (socially and scientifically) the multiple of patients he has to see.

We hug, I almost picking him up off the floor. Then as I descend the stairs in a sort of atrium area, I look up at him and as if in conclusion of our discussion, I state my admiration for his profession (vs. mine) in that he actually HEALS people.

He replies that he at least tries to. "Treats might be the better term."

11/2/12

I dream that I'm awake and on TV or computer there's a program about the values of picture frames. All different kinds are shown, some highly embellished and others plain. The commentator is explaining that because of government regulations regarding nose-blowing, in certain situations (locales) plastic is required and wood frames are forbidden. He and a guest on the program go on to comment about one particular frame and their hope that it doesn't become an industry standard. It's called "White on white". – a white plastic frame in which is a plain white canvas (or paper) "artwork".

Then I'm in a men's room where two others have taken the toilet stalls. As I wait my turn I notice the filth of a semi-concealed urinal, *[this image a strange displacement of the actual appearance of a plate with food-residue on it, and partly covered by other dishes that I actually washed earlier in the evening]*.

12/3/12

I'm sitting on what seems to be a porch overlooking some yachts at docks. Someone comes in and turns a table with a TV on it so he can sit facing it. He turns up the volume. I'm trying to read and eat at the same time, kind of reclined on a beach chair. I comment to someone sitting next to me that I should go get my earphones and Walkman so that the loudness of the TV isn't so distracting.

I look at the person next to me. It's absolutely, unmistakably, the Hispanic *[dock worker who was (actually) fired from work a couple weeks back]*. I'm tempted to ask him how he got his job back, but the activity out on the docks catches my attention. A large group of young men and women, some of them intermixed, others separated by gender are gathered. Behind them at the dock is a magnificent white-hulled craft, somewhat the size of a Coast Guard cutter, but also seemingly a configurational fusion of a ship and a Lincoln Navigator or Cadillac SUV. Rigged as a sail-powered boat, above the white hull the masts and rigging are a combination of glistening black and chrome-color.

I sense that the gathering and boat has something to do with people being inducted into the Coast Guard. But I'm suddenly seeing what's on the TV as I'm walking from the porch. On the screen is a woman's lower body, her legs up in the air, a funnel in her rectum – into which I watch various solutions being poured prior to the addition of some kind of effervescing (even as it goes into the funnel) powder. She begins writhing and moaning.

And I'm next on a bed and at the foot is an elderly, extremely skinny, very Jewish-looking man who I realize must be a gastroenterologist. Suddenly he's up at the head of the bed, as if a parallel of myself in a way, and I touch his hand as his arm drapes down beside mine.

"Are you a Nazi?" I ask him. *(An emailed essay sent to me during the day had concerned Nazis. As for the rest of the kaleidoscopic images ..????)*

For an instant, almost like a flash, there's Christopher Reeve and his wife (only their heads) appear as if in a round frame. Both look as if they're in their eighties.

I awake.

12/5/12

I'm lying on a bed which seems to be strewn with women's apparel. But then I'm suddenly on a lawn on my knees, hugging a golden retriever dog whose owner is warning me that my posture may be upsetting to the pooch. I assure otherwise and the dog seems very affectionate to me.

Next I'm on a street beside which is a length of stone wall. I start peeling a melon (or cantaloupe), the rind-strip thickening and stretching out into the distance of the street and wall. I taste it, but find it pulpy almost to the extent of a gel. I decide it's best not to eat any of the melon.

12/6/12

It seems I'm in a space within an old office building. There had been a pharmacy or medical supply store and the shelves and partitions, some with indistinct objects atop or attached, are still there. I have the feeling that someone I know is going to rent the space and transform it into an apartment (or kind of "loft"). I've had someone (an employee of mine?) lay brick walls like dividers of a corridor into the area, and separations of spaces. The bricks are elongated and yellow and the masonry job is about as bad as can be pictured. The height of the partitioning is about four feet.

With others I leave the area to go out for food and drinks.

But then I am alone, walking along across the front yards of quite expensive houses that face an ocean cove. On the other side are other expensive residences, their lawns also right up to the waterfront. The area bears a resemblance to part of Salem, MA.

Suddenly I've entered a brick-paved parking lot (it seems it's adjacent to the residential area). In this dream I'm aware that in a prior dream I'd been in the same lot, but entered it from a different direction. Beyond and below one side of the lot is a large park. Centered in the many acres is a gazebo, screened-in, and so large as to be almost the proportion of an auditorium.

There are people gathered there to discuss what I hear to be a very contentious matter of whether the park should provide for dogs to run free. Before I enter the building I intercede in a fight between two men, one of whom is carrying a brief case. The other has attacked him, apparently enraged over the dog issue. I lecture the attacker about his "misplaced proportions" – that whether dogs should run free or not is surely not as important as whether people are starving or the ecology of the earth is being ruined. Inside the "gazebo-auditorium" are many very elite-looking people. I walk amongst them, spraying each with the spray bottle (like for Windex) I'm holding.

And then I'm in what appears to be Melrose (near where I lived when I was a kid). There's a variety store *(there was one actually)*, but it suddenly morphs into a barber-shop-type façade. I enter, descend a couple stairs to a kind of lobby area. There are a number of Italian-looking men there, good-naturedly ribbing one for not being able to keep from moving, thus failing to enact a statue or a mime. Further within this place I find Rich (my son) on a bed in what looks to be a hospital or clinic room. He's being released after being an in-patient. Negative results of something. As we leave, I note that he's talking about Angie (my wife, his mother) as if she's still alive and I'm concerned if he's losing his mind.

12/8/12

I approach a vast old factory/mill complex which is located in a valley beside the road I'm on. The road sort of circles downward toward the big brick and wood buildings. Overhead, the sky darkens and soon becomes almost an absolute black with a funnel extending down toward the ground. But there is no feeling of air movement, let alone wind.

I'm talking on the cell phone with the terminal manager of the company I work for *(actually)*. We mention how hazy the sky has been. I describe it as being like you'd expect on an early spring day when the snow is beginning to melt because the air is just starting to get really warm.

Suddenly I'm within one of the factory/mill buildings. It's crowded with other people who have gathered there for some kind of event or meeting. To ascend to the floor where the function is to take place one has to climb stairs which protrude from the walls like veins of a turbine. There's no railing on either side, but by swinging my body I'm able to grasp the tops of cabinets that are located along the walls beside the stairs. Still, I'm very acrophobic as I make my way up slowly, holding up the progression of others behind me.

I find myself in a very large room which was used as a store selling antique furniture and architectural pieces. The company is moving out, most of the merchandise gone. I'm talking with a couple guys who seem to have been the proprietors and we mention their moving after all those years. *(the place seems to relate to a combination of a building wrecking company I used to buy materials from, and an architectural antique/parts dealer to whom I sold materials I'd salvaged and for whom I did some demolition work).* I notice a huge old cast iron wood or coal burning device, but am suddenly considering a king size mattress which is partly standing upright, but slumped over from half-way up. I'm just about to take it when I'm told that someone else has already claimed it because they need it. I reply that I'm glad, for it's better for someone else to make use of it than for me to just take it and store it. *(When I moved from Franklin, I was unable to sell or give away a king size mattress and eventually had to just put it out for the trash collection).*

And finally I find myself, in the dream, in Malden, MA, a small city just north of Boston. I'm on one side of a busy street and on the other a few Hispanic young men are setting up a target in a small parking lot which is unoccupied by cars. But people are walking along the sidewalks and cars are passing on the street. I consider, from my side of the street, that the intention to shoot arrows, across a busy street toward the target, is actually rather dangerous.

12/9/12

I arrive at delivery stop. It's a food warehouse. It's about quarter to one. The appointment is for two. I inquire how long the wait and I'm told it'll be at least two hours, maybe a lot more. There are seven trucks ahead of me. I call in to dispatch and he tells me to just wait. He wants to get rid of the freight. I read through one magazine, finish another, nap, and at about three-thirty I walk back to the office of the warehouse. I remind the girl that I've been out in the lot for a long, long time and hope they haven't forgotten I'm there. She hands me back the paperwork and tells me "It's too late to take this now. You'll have to have your company reschedule delivery." *[This was not a dream!! This actually happened!! Drastic waits are not unusual at grocery warehouses – but to be kept waiting so long and then refused is just, almost criminal. I get paid by the hour, so considered my sojourn "free time on-the-clock". I hope my company charges someone plenty for the wasted wages. And pity the over-the-road drivers who only get paid when the truck is moving (and maybe a "nominal" $25.00 or so per delivery stop. What goes on in the trucking industry is atrocious. Not the stuff of dreams. NIGHTMARES!!*

12/10/12

With someone (wife Angie?) I'm driving towards Brian and Helen's *(nephew and niece)* new place in Foxboro *[during the day, among others I'd made out Xmas card to them]*. But we find the locale to be beside a vast seaside marsh and forest combined, kind of a quagmire with a tidal bore running through it right behind the small, decrepit deck behind the house. The building itself resembles a ramshackle tenement three-decker.

Inside the first floor resembles Terri's *(another niece)* abode. The rooms are filled with people, one a tall, older man holding his head and staggering. The others are twentyish and making out on couches, in closets, in the middle of rooms. A regular orgy, though in the dream I see no nakedness or actual sexual behavior.

Suddenly I'm with Greg *(my son)* in a large cafeteria-like place which becomes filled with young people as if gathering after a sports event. We wait together at a table. Finally a waiter comes along on a golf cart, another to another table on a bicycle. We both order large tuna salad subs, Greg specifying crumbled hard-boiled egg to be on his. He excuses himself to go to the bathroom. I wait. No food comes. No Greg. At a table a bit away I notice that one of the male student (?) crowd is engaged in sexual intercourse with another male. As they go at it, most of the others of the crowd watch and at the end burst into an ovation of applause.

But then the place kind of morphs into the dining hall of a nursing home and I'm sitting next to an elderly woman for whom I'm cutting up some kind of meat on her dinner plate as she tells me about the pancreatic pain she experiences and that nothing can be done about it.

Next, racing along in a VW bug (or similar vehicle). Going uphill and around curves at breakneck speed. The area resembles parts of Rockport or the Maine coast. But not until I've left the vehicle and am walking along a promenade between collegiate-looking brick buildings do I see the ocean. It's far below the cliff atop which the buildings are, and between which I pass through a very ornate cast iron gate.

Outside the gate, gazing at the sea for a second, I seem to be with daughter Chris (or is it grand daughter Sarah)?. We're talking about whether Clinton or Bush, Barack or Mitt, would provide the better leadership in this post-affluent apocalypse of the economy.

12/11/12

I'm holding a camera and in its view screen is a building. I wonder if it's the image of an actual building in Marlboro, or just a similar one somewhere. And suddenly I'm explaining to someone who seems vindictive, that I'm taking a series of railroad pictures (thus the one of the buiding). *[and in this dream, a recapitulation of a former dream concerning pictures and explanation about railroad photo-series].*

Next I'm racing (in some vehicle) through shrubbery, but then over water, and next up and higher until I'm looking down from a satellite perspective. I'm looking down on a partially abandoned fairground (or partially disassembled carnival locale). . . . on which I'm suddenly walking with, perhaps it's Vincent *[one of my grand sons].* We come to a trailer selling fried, powdered-sugar-coated dough. But I have to go back to my car because I left my wallet in it.
[the fried dough may be a shard of memory from an amusement park Angie and the kids and I (sometimes with others) went to a few times. It was there that I had fried dough for the first time in my life].

And then I seem to be looking for a place on Arsenal St. in Watertown, where, if you karate-chopped it on a map you'd find gold. *[another dream-fragment repeated !?!?!]*

12/13/12

I'm in a huge space that could be a warehouse. But it seems it's used as a New England Motor Freight garage facility. The dock doors are being replaced.*[those on the actual terminal building in dire need].* At first it seems that "tilt-up" (or down) doors are being installed. But then I'm seeing intricate bearing, roller, and track systems. I'm suddenly walking across the vast floor with one of the installers and to my query about the price probably being over $2,000 per unit, he responds that they're over $3,000. Off to one side, two girls are behind a counter and one is talking rather loudly about someone being an asshole.

Next I'm driving and towing a boat on a trailer. I'm looking for a place that sells 100 HP motors. Up a long hill and behind a garage-like building I enter a machine-shop/auto-parts-salesroom. Out from a back room an older man comes behind the counter. I notice a strange, shiny (plastic?) brown, bean-like object in one of his nostrils. Mentioning the motor I seek, I notice a couple enter the place and I hear the continuation of classical music I'd been listening to *[as always, in actuality]*. I comment on everyone being "into" classical (and it seems then that the garage-door guy had had classical playing though I'd not "heard" prior to the couple entering the dream sequence.

Leaving the place (which had nothing to do with marine motors), I head off the driveway and over a lawn and down embankments and over rocks and through underbrush. I'm rather concerned about tipping over or damaging my vehicle, but I reach the road. On which I see *[next-door neighbor in Franklin]* Marie's cat's front paw get run over by a car *[actual paw-run-over of a cat happened when I was about 10 and living in Malden, and I was devastated. The poor cat limped ever after]*. But I was able to reach Marie's cat to pick it up. However it escaped my grasp and scurried up into her car – which was partly filled with coarse gravel. Amid it I lost sight of the cat, so was fishing through car contents which included Marie's pocket book. Suddenly she was violently shaking my sleeve, assuming I was a thief. We found the cat. I managed to pick it up, belly-upward, and nestle it in a kind of oversized cardboard hotdog sleeve.

And then I was with Richard and two women, one his ex-girlfriend with whom I was making out up to a point of intimate touching. She stopped me, citing some reticence (or delay interim) before she'd be ready to resume anything sexual in her life. Rich and the other woman were just there. But then he and I were outside, it seemed on the road at the foot of the hill I'd earlier descended from my quest for the 100 HP motor. I'm trying to clean the clouded lens of my camera *[driving home from work, the glass in my pickup truck had started clouding up with condensation]*. He's suddenly warning me that I'm going to be charged with assault and battery – and I instantly worry that he's "projecting" – that he's the one about whom he's talking ("in my image"). As for the camera, my dabbing Windex on its view screen alarms him, and the surface at first turns translucent green *[although I don't really see color, nor did I really hear music in other part of the dream]*. But suddenly the viewer is pristine clean.

12/15/12

It's a decrepit, ancient, brick building that may once have been part of a factory or mill complex. It stands now forlorn, alone within an overgrown expanse where other buildings had been and either burned down or been torn down *[this imagery derives from a locale in Millville, MA that I hiked through with a grand son]*

I've been hired to affix metal plates over the openings where windows used to be. I'm up on rickety wooden scaffolding and have just successfully fastened the first plate. Seems that I'd done this the previous year, for the bolt holes line up. But on down a bit, there's been a doorway added beside the window opening. So the plate doesn't cover the now-greater opening.

Without having solved that second-story problem, I find myself inside the building on the ground. There's no upper floor, the height of the dismal place towering above. Within, there's *[as in a previous dream]* what appears to be the combination of a huge blender, and some kind of boiler or furnace. Beside this, a three-story high Sonatube is standing upright on an old horse-drawn wagon (no horse) until it tips over, soundlessly falling to a horizontal position.

But then suddenly I'm driving a tractor-trailer rig in the industrial area of Worcester, MA. I turn into a lot which appears to once have been fully occupied, but the buildings razed except for a couple kicked-out remains of small structures, one resembling a bus. Inside these, as I use the lot in which to make a U-turn, I notice there are a great number of small cave-like spaces penetrating into otherwise solid filling *[and, even in the dream, I realize I'm seeing the transposed image of cave dwellings. Myriad of these were pictured in a recent National Geographic magazine].*

For a few nights I was aware of dreaming, but not of what I was dreaming other than as if through some sort of veil which allowed only the faintest imagery of sensing, not of senses. On waking, there was really nothing to record – other than what I've just written in this paragraph..

12/20/12

Clear imagery of the inside of a staircase. It's in a separate structure from another building, as if a semi-self-standing stairwell (kind of like a square "turret"). On three sides were very large windows, but there was substantial surface of v-groove pine board paneling as wall surface. Apparently I was supposed to make a delivery of some kind of freight which would require me to ascend the stairs. But before I'd be allowed to do that, I'd been told I'd have to paint the interior of the stair well, which I was refusing to do.

But I was suddenly in a crowded consignment or antique or second-hand shop, looking at a $35 laptop and other objects. Outside there was police activity that had something to do with one of my grand daughters not wanting to go somewhere (back to college?).

But then I was seeing a wizened Asian man violently reprimanding another of the drivers *[actual]* from work – regarding reckless driving of the truck or something.

12/21/12

A very brief interlude regarding some group (truck drivers? Students?) flipping a coin. If one side came up, a tree would be cut down immediately If the other side, the tree would continue to stand for the remainder of its natural life.

12/22/12

It seemed to be the preparation for some kind of media event. In a broad corridor, separated from a function hall or theater area by double doors, someone among a group that seemed to be Jewish, was discussing with others that I should screw his grandmother.

Already in the main area the event is taking place. Someone's on the stage lecturing about the Blue Ridge Parkway and other governmental projects. Someone else (Angie?) and I are to join some sort of a panel of others on the stage. But to do so, we have to literally climb over people. One of them is Hillary Clinton. We manage to do this, somewhat disrupting the presentation.

No sooner are we seated than the event concludes, the audience departing, but a number of participants milling around. Some are complaining about how terrible things had gone, that Einstein had been so upset he didn't even have the courtesy to say goodbye to anyone.

But the conclusion of another is that even though the funding for the highway wasn't allocated, there was plenty of gas to be pumped. And it was a gas pump image that concluded this dream. *[various bits and pieces of reality were involved – Einstein from an ebook I received on his life, the confused event inspired by a book I'm reading on the rock group The Who, and the chaos of their performances and personal lives. The Blue Ridge Parkway came into the collage from the collection of my own emails and essays I'd read over just before going to sleep. Nothiing Freudian here – just the brain being picked-over in somewhat random perusal of and picking from – a landfill (which, along with waste and recycling etc., comprised the contents of several of my emails and essays!!]*

12/23/12

I emerge from an unseen building. Before me is a structure of which only the upper part is detailed in the dream. It looks like the steeple of a church – a spire at very top set upon a kind of cupola base, all four sides of which are transparent so that it kind of morphs into an aquarium. In it are various rather hideous organisms, indistinct. Very clear and detailed is an almost transparent "crayfish" *(is the only way I can describe its morphology)* kind of plastered onto one of the windows, fully top to bottom, thus a huge critter. Behind it, floating in the water, I clearly see a parrot and also some kind of animal that appears to be cuddling a koala.

Next, with unseen others I'm in what looks to be the remains of a long- abandoned and mostly collapsed amusement park. Only fragments of walls are standing here and there. But there's also a chain-link fenced-in area in which the Toyota pickup truck I used to own *[actually]* and the Olds *I actually inherited from Aunt Marj* are confined.along with at least one other unidentified and decrepit vehicle.

I'm on the phone with someone at an auto repair facility. Another of my vehicles is there, and the mechanic is telling me I'd better get down there and see just how bad things are – apparently the car is not repairable to pass inspection or something. The Olds is being extricated from the enclosure. Outside, I get inside. It's being driven by one of the truck drivers from work *[actual]*. My admonition that he'd better go immediately and get gas (tank's reading empty) is scoffed. More important to him is to pick up supplies for some picnic or other (company ?) affair. We're heading for a super market, but come upon a roadside stand selling potatoes and vegetables etc.

We stop. I almost fall over a huge, black plastic rubbish bag. We approach the provisions displayed for sale, but come to a gigantic valise or garment case beside the road (as if out for the rubbish) In it and around it, making it jounce and jiggle, there's a veritable "swarm" of ducklings, all chirping boisterously. Off to one side there's another pile of animals, one of them about half-actual size donkey. A tiny (like a true miniature – large Hummel size) baby donkey keeps climbing up on the pile of animals surrounding the half-sized donkey – and getting kicked off to one side where he somewhat morphs into a puppy with a bulging little belly. He keeps landing on his back, and giggling like a baby for a few seconds. Then he uprights and climbs back on the mount of writhing creatures. None of these others is seen distinctly *[but are probably "concept" – not image – transitions from the prior ducklings]*.

Freud? Jung? Karen? Anyone got an analysis here? Cognitive recombinance? Almost random??

`1/24

At first it seemed I was flying low over a tenement area (interspersed two and three story mostly frame buildings) somewhat suggesting the Lechmere Square, Cambridge region.

But I was then in an industrial area back lot paved with gravel large enough to almost be "rip-rap". I attempted to place a rather large, and damaged, carton into a truck (or my pickup truck) from a loading dock. Inside the carton were small (household fire extinguisher size) canisters of something or other. The carton ripped more, but I got it and its contents into the vehicle.

On the wide, straight road (again resembling through parts of Cambridge, I noticed that a couple of the canisters had fallen out of the truck. But for some reason I kept going, assuming that I could just pick up the dropped ones on my way back.

But on the way back they were gone. I continued, now driving through what seemed to be somewhat a fusion of images: Weymouth Landing, MA *(where my first wife and I had lived in her parents' home)* . . and Franklin, Ma *(from which I'd moved a couple years ago after living there for @40 years)*.

In the dream, now walking at that location, specifically I was leaving the yard "next door" to "my" house in Franklin. Next door there had been Marie's (and family) *home [I'd made a Xmas phone call to Marie just a few hours earlier]*. I was crossing the yard between the houses (which now seemed to have a kind of access road to somewhere bisecting the yards. On the other side "my" house now stretched from front to back to include what stretched out to be an almost one-story factory size structure, inclusive of commercial-size garage doors..

This fusion of "my" house and industrial-park-property-properties . . . now belonged to the family of my first wife!!! I skulked through an opening (kind of vehicular passageway) about midway from front to back of the elongate building, made my way to the front, determined no one was home, and let myself in. Having slept on the couch *(quite definitely an image-transfer of my own)* I awoke, relieved that no one was home yet, and began to affix some kind of thin drape or curtain to one side of the window behind the couch *[earlier in the day I'd fashioned a piece of foam rubber long enough to fit a space between my kitchen cabinets through which cold air seeped]*.

Next I gathered up a bunch of loose threads and shards of cloth from the curtain, noticed that my sock had left a rust stain on the couch cover about which I could do nothing. I was in a hurry to leave and did so.

The dream ended in the big-gravel-paved lot where it had begun. Others were picking up spilled pieces of freight beside the big, torn carton. But it wasn't canisters. They were picking up and re-packaging small boxes containing some kind of electrical components.

I was very much relieved.

12/27/12

I'm outside a large building that could either be a commercial garage or a barn. I've stopped a managerial looking guy who's driving a golf cart, my hand on the front of the cart. I've just said something very clever, which in the dream both he and I were impressed by, but on awakening I have no recollection of.

But I continue with him, it seems as a salesman for a device that provides protection in case of a customer running out of oil in his tank. For one thing, it will provide for temporary heat (until a delivery) without any oil needed. And it's also insurance that a burner technician won't be needed to re-prime (etc) the furnace after a delivery after a run-out. For this company the cost would only be $14.00 per month (apparently per customer).

Next I'm in a recording studio *[this dream fragment deriving from book I'm reading about the Rock musician group, The Who]* . . .where a musical ad is being recorded, along with a "jingle" to promote the above device. I suggest that for another company under consideration as customer, it might be good to raise the key signature of the music up a half-tone.

Suddenly I've stopped another guy driving another golf cart *[the golf cart comes from 1) the means by which manager of a huge warehouse, where I make frequent deliveries, gets around the sprawling facility – and prior to going to sleep, a "commuta-car" concept I'd mentioned in some of my writing that I was extracting excerpt from]*.

The second guy on the second cart is protesting that his is a much smaller company than the first, and therefore the $14 would be too expensive. I suggest $7.

And suddenly it seems I'm in a little shop (ice cream? Coffee?) that could be in an ocean-front (like Rockport, MA) location. Next, with me there is an obviously Jewish woman *[resembling the picture of author of a book I'm reading]*. But then we're walking along outside along a path with stones for footsteps. But then we're lying down next to each other, it seems half-way up a wall. We're not making out, but there's something suggestive and mention is made that if we keep going at this rate we may get to sexuality.

At the foot of a staircase as I listen, she's explaining to someone that a "kipper", in Hebrew legend, is the term for a heroine (it seems somehow relating to herself in this case. I then consider that "kippered herring must be fish prepared by a Hebrew heroine . . . as long as she's not on heroin."

And then I'm walking past junked vehicles and other immense proportion construction or military size equipment beside a road – until I come to what looks like the wrecked remains of a pontoon recreational boat which suddenly morphs into what looks like an extremely ravaged, tipped, torn diner (probably originally an actual streetcar). Inside it are remnants revealing that people lived there. Outside it I find myself driving my tractor-trailer rig off the highway onto a little dirt spur that dead-ends. There's a car there, two young women, and I motion for them to move their vehicle. They do and I pull forward, the cab upward until I'm looking down into a valley and across a vast panorama.

I move a couple objects in the cab so that I can lie down and go to sleep.

Next I dream some fragments involving Terri [an in-law who's dying from cancer], money for her terminal and funeral needs, whether my money is in short supply, and Buddha. My late wife, Angie, and someone else (her niece?) seem to be confusing the Buddhist Buddha with an actor who goes by that name, but spelled Budda. The "fusion" confusion comes from an actual delivery I made during the previous day. The freight receiver at the place goes by the name Buddha because of his physical resemblance (big belly, round face, placid persona) to the religious icon.   12/27 was a busy dream-night.

12/28/12

First, wandering around in a huge hall or exhibition building with a continuous counter all around the outside walls. On it are objects, tchotchkes, ephemera, modules, toys, appliances, antiques, junk. At one point my grand son Nicholas is trying to make an electric drill (which is fastened to a plaque) stay adhered to the wall above the counter.

Angie (my late wife) is apparently going to go on a solo camping trip but the car we have isn't adequate. I go out, purchase an older convertible, and come back. Also, I've obtained a dog. As soon as I come into the yard, my grand sons, Nicholas and Vincent, come out to see the vehicle. The dog jumps out, shrinks in size, and darts into a hole in a big tree.

Finally (it seems) I'm dreaming about publishing or presenting some papers or performances of others. I get $1,000 from each. Some legal entity (or person) gets $600 each from me for his services. I consider this a bit usurious and awake.

12/29/12

There's a trailer that's backed into a warehouse. It's much closer to one side of the narrow opening than the other, and the wider space has something to do with the glimpse of "morphology of a lithe young girl". In our suppressive culture, this kind of alluring prurience has to be concealed by elastics or ligatures or tourniquets or bandages, bandaids, bandanas, or even completely by burqas (and images of same on an arm or leg flash in the dream).

Then I'm standing on a vast loading dock and looking down into a commercial food preparation (or kitchen) area. The manager there is wearing a bath robe with a large blotch of something on the back. I'm carrying a book which I put down on a table which is floating in air beside the loading platform. A couple guys come up to me, and we begin talking. They're asking whether my arrangement *[4 days at full-time status in actuality at work]* results in my giving up part of my vacation or personal-day time. I tell them it doesn't, part of the reason being that "though I don't want to seem egotistical, I'm valuable enough to the company that they want me to keep working. And in our negotiations of my status I told them if this couldn't be arranged, I'd just retire completely."

Finally we're reminiscing about roadside dangers and I tell about going out Route 20, turning left to go to the Marriott food warehouse, leaving there and taking the back road through the fields . . . crossing a small bridge of a stream a massive timber comprising a significant part of the bridge structure that just recently fell off.

12/31/12

Intimately caressing Angie, who seems to be asleep. Thinking that this is the first time we've been so sensually compatible, and that it isn't too late for this to be the start of an enhanced relationship.

Suddenly I'm cleaning out accumulation from the back of my pickup truck. The area then becomes more like a very low shed than anything on a vehicle. In it are large pieces of crumpled felt, and a plywood box with sliding doors which, when removed, reveal another set of doors and then another and another. But finally I get to the inside contents which seem to be Bonnie and Nick and Vincent and others (including Rich?) coming back from Vermont. They've successfully sold their house there.

I'm in a barn with a middle aged guy wearing coveralls. He's stocky, cranky, wears metal-rimmed glasses, and must have been interviewing applicants for some TV program he heads. His wife is involved but unseen. I watch one guy audition as if through a small duct (leading from the main barn room to where I am . . . . hiding?) The guy in charge becomes enraged and literally hurls the other toward me and any barrier through which the "duct" had passed disappears and I'm going to be flattened by the flying body.

But back to the guy in the barn, now with his son. The 30ish son is fat, a classic redneck. For the program, he's demonstrating his hunting ability. First he has a rifle which he hurls through an amazing distance to spear the water next to where a bird is floating. Another bird comes flying in over the lake and drops dead next to the one floating. Then something else (a rock?) is used as the weapon/ammunition combined.

The lake is still there, but now I'm with two young Hungarian Jewish scientists. They're researching and developing some kind of communication or transmission system. I'm installing it out into and across under the lake. It consists of a significant number of every extension cord, telephone wire, TV antenna wire, etc. etc. that I can remember having owned. And thus I notice that in some places, the wire being somehow pulled from my locus to wherever it's going . . . isn't a continuum. Extension cords don't plug into
TV antenna wires. Phone wires aren't compatibly connected to 220 volt appliance cords, etc. etc. Heedless of getting my shoes and pants wet, I hasten out into the water to correct the problems.

[The kaleidoscope of ideas and images in this dream come from sources beyond analytical recollection. But a couple are obvious. One, the Hungarian Jewish researchers: during the day I'd looked up some information and written some material on the famous group who'd been involved in the Manhattan Project and other ultra-echelon mathematical and scientific pursuits. The TV show/hillbilly/barn sequence just takes person (from a picture in Forbes) and place (a barn converted into a living room) and other "image-shards" and fuses them into a mosaic of context (TV show – which includes oblique reference to weapons/guns/deriving from articles read (and that I wrote, too) regarding the Conn. shootings.) Freudian or even Jungian content in such dream-collage? Bullshit!! It's scan-scavenging the "landfill of the unconscious.)

2013

1/1/13

First, walking with Richard along a broad valley, a tiny brook to one side and overflow of standing water amid grass and reeds through which we trek.

Then inside what could be a derelict mansion *[here, some imagery from a book I'd just begun reading on the architecture of insane asylums. But this first specific scenario places the section of structure along a drive very much like that of an industrial building that adjoins a railroad line in Andover]*.

There's either demolition or remodeling going on, and it seems that Rich has been living (or working) there. But we're suddenly out in a yard behind the place. The ground slopes down and strewn all around are structural parts and mechanical things. We gather one or another of them and ascend to an outbuilding which resembles a carriage house. Others are taking object into this, but some are removing them – such as the two pieces of long, black molding that someone passes to me.

Next, as if in a small meeting, Rich and I are commenting on a projected spreadsheet that lists various aspects of what our (it seems collaborative) enterprise is involved in (such as construction) and not (such as ice cream vending).

Looking across a city street at potential real estate interest (it seems the interest is to rent space in which to conduct our business). Then I'm in the first floor of the place, occupied by a bakery or delicatessen. I talk with the woman behind the counter. Back on the original side of the street I obtain paper and pen and cross again. I'm in my pajamas. There's different young woman now behind the counter and I ask her to please write down the phone number and a contact name on the paper. After dropping it several times she hands it back to me with the information, scribbled almost illegibly amid orders for food.

Still there, a short woman appears behind the counter and asks if I recognize her – that she'd lived in the house sold near where I'd lived *[and here, not imaged but semi-cognated, I sensed a fusion of Lincoln St., Melrose where I'd lived as a kid, and Franklin, MA]*. Still in the same place I overhear another young woman talking about what she wishes she'd become (I guess rather than what she actually has) . . . and I embrace her, turn her as we lean against a refrigerator, and tell her that I always wanted to be a ballerina, but I became self-employed and that's why I'm still in my pajamas in the middle of the day in a delicatessen.

From back across the street I survey the building, realizing that all the floors are occupied.

1/3/13

Vivid image of going steeply downhill on a street much resembling one in Malden's west end. Victorian houses line the way. Angie seems to be with me.

Suddenly just vague impressions that I'm dreaming. One is that I'm on a sleigh ride over snow drifts (or sand bags) *[this probably reiterates Prokofiev's "Lieutenant Kije Suite"'s sleigh ride movement which I'd heard a couple days prior]*. Several other "senses" of dream content were subliminal.

But then I dreamed that I awoke and it was necessary to write down the dream material before it sunk into mind's oblivion (or was superimposed by consciousness). And I dreamed that I realized that my being awake (for I had the pad of paper and pen in hand) was an illusion, for I was still asleep. This confusion of state seemed to compound a couple times like being in between two "mirrors of actuality" (was I asleep and dreaming of being awake – or awake and thinking about still being asleep and dreaming about . . . . .)

1/4/13

I seem to be in some kind of senior facility or rest home in Dorchester. Very vague assumption, fleeting glimpses of structure interior *[from book I'm reading on 1800s insane asylum architecture]*. With someone unseen I climb out a window onto the roof of a carport and jump down onto a picnic table's bench, while commenting on how beautiful a place it is. For some reason I've sold or traded my step van *[owned years ago]* here and set out to get to work.

Going up hill in residential area. I find a bar of soap stuck to my back. I'm kicking a ball or something. On up I go, finally coming to open area which appears to be adjacent to Southeast Expressway in the Milton area (except in that area the land is a tidal marsh – and in my dream the region is very high with a view of the distant ocean to the East.

At that point I'm aware that I'm heading in the wrong direction (South) and will be late for work. *[and I wonder if having purchased a "smart-phone" earlier on 1/4, thus entailing a higher monthly bill, though I'd previously determined to curtail all spending . . . . was the actual "wrong way" that this dream so convolutedly represented: my old age . . . the phone has a map Ap!!]*

1/5/13

First I'm on a somewhat crowded bus *[vague transposition of imagery from Beetles' movie?]* People standing in the aisle due to insufficient seating. Guy sitting next to me and I are smoking, our cigarettes down to tiny butts. We both drop them and he's having difficulty finding his.

Next I'm in a car driving up mountainous road *[imagery of 190 between Worcester and Leominster—which I'd traversed going the other direction last night]*. In the distance are somewhat Alpine elevation peaks of bare rock. As I drive there's a discussion going on about human morality and with such beauty there's no need for violence and war *[transposed from dissertation a grand son had with me regarding society's standards]*.

As if having reached the summit of the highway in above paragraph *[also, imagery here from the parking lot of the Jordan's Furniture Store in Reading, Ma]* I approach the entrance to an arena. There's a ticket or concession counter. I'm standing at it beside a couple who I hear talking about how the company they both work for has paid for their trip and is giving them money to extend it even through Europe *[ideation/imagery here from a pamphlet on world waterway tours that came in my mail and I'd looked through with awe – at the scenery and prices]*. I comment to these people that they're most fortunate for the opportunity. To their question, I respond that I left on my excursion that morning and the next day would have to be at work.

1/6/13

I arrive early to deliver a load of beer. I pass through a gate into an industrial yard surrounded by warehouses. It appears no one is there yet, so I read a couple pages, then nap.

I'm next walking to the back of the trailer. I open the doors. Inside the doors there's another set of doors. I open them. Inside them there's a barrier from side to side and top to bottom of the trailer and I wonder if there's actually a beer load or if empty space is being hid.

Suddenly I'm inside one of the warehouse buildings where a few men have arrived for work. They acknowledge that I'm there with their beer load and will unload me soon. But I'm climbing a set of stairs up into what seems to be the office area. I open a door because I need to throw something away. A woman behind a desk directs me to the rubbish barrel.

The barrel is a 50 gallon drum with a table top on it and a guy in work clothes and I are both leaned over with our elbows on this barrel-top table. He informs me that he's not just a warehouseman. He's also a part-time scholar.

And suddenly I'm dissertating to him *[in the dream essentially what I'm writing here]* about the creativity of the human mind being evidence that by Darwinian evolution alone existence can't be explained. My example is a symphony orchestra. It's composed of a vast variety of instruments that were invented separately by individuals here and there. There was no concerted or organized effort to "invent a symphony orchestra". Thus when one considers that all those disparate parts were brought together as a vastly complex sonic system (the orchestra) – and in all parts of the world – and that various individuals composed symphonic music . . . . the cohesive (and beyond that, the aesthetic-unto-visual-and-emotional effect upon the audience) **whole** is so much greater than the mere sum of its parts . . . that "exponential synergy" is the term I've coined for the amazing, enthralling phenomenon.

And there's no selective (survival-fitness or reproductive proliferation) advantage at all to inventing a musical instrument, composing music for it, or playing it in an ensemble of whatever size. Musical performances, even classical, do not involve survival – nor result in gene-proliferation by resulting in audience orgies.

And even one more consideration: Such combination of sonic variants within a context of actually mathematical frequency matrices (key signatures, tempos, transitions, chord structures) . . . . is obviously not the "outcome" of any "descent with modification" over generations and eons. It's a "creationistic" phenomenon, as a whole within hardly 250 years – and in specific "leaps" of form and format

(Palastrina, Handel, Hayden, Wagner, Tchaikovsky, Prokofiev, Bernstein . . . . "quantum-unto-dimension" leaps of orchestration and intonation and more.

    This example, as with so many other areas of human creation – reveals a design inherent in existence, emerging almost as spontaneity of inference, discovery, invention, implementation, synergic-combination, finally actualization and implementation A symphony orchestra is just one example.

[and in my dream as I was talking to the guy, what I was saying was almost exactly as I've written just above!!]

1/10/13
    Driving along a high road with massive "cottages" here and there overlooking astounding, distant ocean views.

    But suddenly I'm in my rig going up a little hill in a congestion of Lowell (perhaps) and, hearing sirens. I pull up onto a cement center island to get out of the way. An ambulance passes, but as I proceed, I come upon a police cruiser with the same configuration of flashing lights as the ambulance. Cops are on the sidewalk along with a very light-skinned, obese, naked Negro man who looks absolutely humiliated.

    Next I'm in a corridor with benches on one side and a wooden handrail all along which, at one point, I bite. But I continue on to the end of the corridor where there's a little access window. I push a doorbell button next to the window and, within, is Dr. McGovern *[someone I actually dealt with]* and I'm making, not an appointment for consultation, but it seems arrangements to have dinner or some other social situation..

    But I realize I have to attend to something else first. And I'm now in a large area that could be a very shoddy amusement-area building or concourse – or discount store. As I walk through the place with someone (unseen), we're commenting on how all the value of life, such as heritage, art, substance, complexity, has been thrown out for the sake of such plastic and spastic quick-sale shit.

    As I'm about to leave the area I stop where two groups have been contestants in some kind of retro-singing contest. At one end of a long seat are four black girls. At the other, standing and singing, are four white guys doing accappella performance. It ends up the guys win and although I feel bad for the girls (who I didn't hear perform), it seems that the "Four-Seasons-ish" act of the guys was very good.

    Unable to get to my arranged meeting with Dr. McGovern, I'm eating an ice cream and contemplating some kind of candy purchase at what seems to be a resort-area concession stand. I call Chris from there and after she tells me that she must be doing well to have all her data so organized, I arrange when I'll get to her house.

[I can trace almost each and every one of the "conceptual shards" in this dream to simple (non-Freudian, non-Jungian) "filed" observations of "trivia".
There was a doorbell button to ring to get access to a loading dock where I made a delivery the previous day. The corridor with bench and window at end derives from description in a book I just finished on insane asylum buildings and interior design. Ice cream and candy concession from long, long ago in Kennebunkport, Maine. Shoddy concourse or discount store was image of a Walmart where I'd made a purchase a couple days prior. The acappella singers sitting on the bench? On PBS a couple weeks ago, classic 50s era DVDs of Black singing groups was

being promoted in fund raising. My biting the hand rail in the insane asylum-ish corridor eludes a "reference" origin in simple observational experience – and would, no doubt, elicit someone's analysis of something "syndromic" about me).]

1/11/13

Far below and beyond a broad bend of a river flowing between steep banks. A sense of (no images) being in an apartment that son Richard and his family occupied in R.I. many years ago *[actually]*.

His son *[my grand son]* Vinnie has been manifesting psychological problems, including statements about doing away with himself. I'm suddenly notified of a serious situation and find myself along with some others in a bathroom. We push aside the shower curtain. The tub is half full of water. Submerged appears to be Vinnie, somewhat shrunken, his face contorted to almost look like some kind of plumbing or pneumatic juncture device (where his mouth would be there's a kind of "nipple" on which one might attach a hose).

One of the others (his brother, Nick?) says that he tried CPR and mouth-to-mouth but was unable to revive Vinnie. All are on the verge of reacting to a tragedy when it's realized that the "body" in the tub is but a dummy made up of shoes, pants, shirt, and the hideous head atop.

Still dreaming, I wonder if the dream represents anything ominous, predictive, premonitory . . and if my reaction should be troubled concern. I conclude that since I'm not experiencing any dream-state anxiety or trauma that there's no "threat" involved. Just a collage-of –conceptuality.

1/12/13

It's a huge paved area *[actually behind a warehouse to which I deliver several times a week]* On one side is the immense building, against which trucks, side-by-side, are backed into the receiving doors. Most of the drivers sit in the trucks while others unload their freight.

I'm standing in the middle of the lot . . . . naked.

Next a college campus. First I'm walking through an administration building and being warned it's getting late. Then I'm outside the quadrangle area and heading into the distance. But suddenly I'm walking back toward the buildings. I notice a single artist's paint brush on the ground. I go up a couple stairs and through a little passageway and across a bit of the grounds. Outside a building there are numerous students. I enter the building and as others admonish my trespass at such late hour, I rush through and exit on the other side just as the doors are being secured.

As if in the same campus, I find myself with another guy *[actual receiver of freight at the abovementioned warehouse]*. He and I see a man standing in a line and "receiver" exclaims, "Eddie Coy!!" *[an actual close childhood friend with whom there's been no contact at all for @ 60 years. In the dream I'm wondering how receiver would recognize and know Eddie]*. I approach where the two are standing together and, yes, sure looks like Ed . . . and I'm just about to ask where he's been for so long. He says, "I'm not Eddie Coy. My name is Wayne." He's friendly about it, and starts to walk away. I mention that there's a bi-part blurring involved: on the one hand, people's appearance changes as they age'; on the other, eyesight becomes less accurate.

Next, with others who seem just vaguely to represent my first wife's family, I'm climbing stairs in a building must be part of the college. On the outside there's a huge opening and I'm commenting that I miss the window (considering that it was stained glass mosaic) but that the clear view to the outside is impressive and refreshing.

Suddenly I'm in a crowded upstairs apartment with people of various cultures and ethnicities, now "related" as in-laws. We kind of drain down the stairs and spew out the recessed front door onto a lawn where there's a fancy picnic procedure taking place. One child is misbehaving and an Anglo mother is trying to deal with it by "parental therapeutics". An elderly Asian who's pushing a baby carriage walks briskly beside me, stating that in such situations, a substantial physical discomfort is the best for the brat-brain.

To one side of there's a fence behind which there are tigers (that look, in the dream, more like feline bodies with [the movie] gremlin heads. They're cute, but it seems might attack either each other or the people assembled.

Having entered that area and avoided the "cats", others (unseen) and I come upon a man who has speared a huge boa-constrictor-like snake through with a pitchfork tine just behind its head. The man is wearing a metallic mask which has a turning propeller at the front (perhaps to swish away the rotten breath of the severely suffering snake). And to make cruel matters worse, the guy is in the process of placing a huge bee on the snake's nose to sting it. In some way as the dream ends I'm reassured that the snake has been rescued.

In what may seem an image fragment of a shopping mall *[reality to which I occasionally deliver]*. To one side there are stores, to the other there's a large enclosed food court. I'm standing with a couple Asian people, involved (as we wait for something) in conversation about how the Hispanic immigration in Japan is threatening to make the Japanese language extinct (or at least obsolete).

And finally I'm under a complicated wooden deck and stairs structure where I'm touching-up black paint that has little blotches or streaks of the under-coat white showing. It seems the owner of the place wants me to paint the whole thing (including a ramshackle building overhead) and I don't want to and wouldn't have the time otherwise. But this "underneath" scenario is then a cellar room in which Richard *[one of my sons]* had been living. But it now appears abandoned, shelving empty, everything askew.

> *Almost all the "bits" of image and ideation in all the above I could identify from sources such as places (the warehouse and staircase beside which is huge windowless opening, even elements of the under-deck and cellar). A tiny Asian woman was my neighbor. My in-law family has become quite multi-cultural. The quadrangle of the college (whose building I enter just at its closing) was almost a "sight-snapshot" of the Cummins Center Complex in Salem, Ma. The tigers? A recent article in National Geographic – their heads? I watched Gremlins II last week. The snake being pitch forked??? Well, along with the stinging and the guy wearing the propellar'd mask . . I recognize fragments and shards from quite a few "resources" recently and in retrospect . . . all brought together in mind-melange. Fascinating, huh??*

1/15/13

I'm one of a whole bunch of people moving stuff from a 2nd floor apartment. We're stuffing all kinds of things into bags and cartons. I find myself holding on to two very large boxes. One is filled with linens and blankets, the other sliced bread to the very top. These at-least-steamer-trunk-size boxes are almost pulling me along behind them. With the boxes I rapidly slide down a staircase as if it were a ski-jump ramp. As I descend I'm gleefully yelling, "Here come the file-esters!!"

At the foot we exit the building onto a cement walk sloping down. On it are boxes and bags from upstairs. At the foot of the ramp several stairs descend to the street level. At the side of the street, people in other houses have put out rubbish to be picked up and I realize the wisdom of leaving the containers of moving material (boxes and bags) on the upper walk.

On the other side of the street, down a steep embankment, there's a body of water.

But suddenly I'm walking back from an apparently abandoned and partially demolished amusement park. Others, unseen, are with me and we're kicking very large leaves off the sidewalk onto a bordering dirt strip from which gnarled tree roots emerge.

I reach the few steps from the sidewalk and go on into the building and up to the second floor where I find myself loading stuff for others to take downstairs. I come across little boxes, some transparent plastic ones which contain various hardware as well as a large number of quarters. I pocket the quarters. My ex-wife Diana is there and I sense that "she won't cook me meat". I'm relieved that she hasn't changed.

Again with two very large cartons I'm sailing down the stairs, yelling for others to get out of the way as I slide on down the walk and land at the foot of the few stairs down to the street level.

Suddenly we're all startled by the sound *[unheard in the dream – "sound" that I dream in any dream is almost never actually audible]* of something as if ripping and crashing and then splashing. We all turn and look in the direction of the amusement park ruins. A round-cheeked, red-nosed, curly-haired plastic head, at least two stories tall, has just toppled into the water and it's drifting very slowly toward us. Its mouth is a huge round gape above a sagging lower lip, and the effect as it also slowly sinks a bit, is that it's gulping the water.

Intending a succinct newspaper headline I phrase to myself and others of the group I'm in, **"GIANT HEAD DRAINS LOCAL LAKE"** !!

[Just a couple most obvious "references" – I keep hardware in clear plastic containers. I keep quarters for the Laundromat in a transparent plastic jar. Some time ago I was in some food facility where a large bin was filled with bread slices that were being sent to a pig farm due to expiration date or something. The tree in front of house I lived in had huge leaves, the roots resembled those of a picture in a Geographic I read a few months ago. As for the giant head . . . . . . got me. But I've been in, by, online about, and written concerning abandoned amusement parks. The succinct newspaper headline related to a DVD where the main character was a neophyte reporter (the move title, "Shipping News".]

The above was part one of that night's dreams. I do believe I was laughing at the head imagery .as I dreamt. Awake, I was laughing as I wrote the above on my ever-ready pad of paper. I went back to sleep. And dreamed the following . . . .

It seemed like I was on Washington Street, Eggleston Square (a slummy part of Boston). I miss my turn onto Columbus Ave, but am able to cut through the grass center strip to get onto Columbus (there's no center strip on Washington St.). But I find myself on the upper level of an immense, multi-building industrial complex, old, decrepit, but still in operation for something or other unknown. But part of the structures is gone, leaving just patches of decaying concrete slabs and remnants where walls were torn down.

I find a set of double doors and enter one of the gray, metal-sided buildings. Two men in expensive suits pass me as I enter a freight elevator whose other occupant recognizes me from a beverage delivery I made to another facility on the South Shore.

On the ground level I exit the elevator and emerge from a kind of alley that wends its way between the old buildings. With no transition from being on foot I'm then in my tractor-trailer rig and the alley has become a vehicular passageway. To one side a strange looking girl with astoundingly beady eyes stops me and says something about my unloading my newspaper load.

But then I'm inside a building, it seems upstairs, and on a protruding sort of porch. Outside, seen through the windows, is some kind of horrific view that a group of people (including me) are forcing some guy to look at, thus to realize the sickness of his family background *[this from the abovementioned movie – the "family" (ancestors) had been pirates, murderers, and worse]*. Outside the window are ghoulish loonies, only one actually seen – a female, the guy's sister?

But then I'm alone and driving my rig slowly in the inner labyrinth between the complex buildings. There's the strange, beady-eyed girl again.
I stop. She says *[unheard but known to me]* "I told you I'd unload your papers".

A third segment. A group of college-aged people in a classroom. They've been told to: "compute Christmas in your heads" – but been given calculators. At the end of the allotted time it's discovered that only Alex has written down a wrong answer, revealing that he cheated and used the calculator. For, unknown to the group members, each of the calculators was programmed to yield erroneous results.

[Alex is an old high school friend with whom I'm in touch now by email exchange. An actual experiment with faulty calculators was conducted some years back in some graduate (MIT) level group. They were told to use the calculators to get the results of various extremely complicated mathematical and physics problems given. The errors resulting were from very slight to quite obvious. The article I read revealed that out of some 30 subjects in the experiment only a couple noticed the discrepancies. The others just punched in the data and wrote down the results, blind to any scrutiny or perspective other than the "implicit infallibility" of technology].

And in a fourth segment of a very busy dream night I've exited, it seems, the Mass Pike and I'm passing through a town. Along a main street that slopes gently down and around a bend, are various houses and buildings. All appear at least 80 years old and some of colonial era (once houses, now converted to stores or offices). Most have been damaged, especially by fire, especially their roofs where patches of mismatched shingles reveal prior chop-through.

A companion unseen and I comment how the huge, over-the-road trucks are racing through the street. The speed limit is 40. In another similar city, it would be 20. We come to an intersection. On the left there's a decrepit building that I recognize *[from an actual place in Fitchburg],* and as we turn onto another street, behind this front structure I see (and the guy tells me) that a vast warehouse structure has been torn down. It leaves a gaping pit some 3 stories deep, which stretches out beyond the remains of foundation and floor at the corner.

Along the sidewalk edge of the precipice there's a very inadequate fence. My companion decides to walk down into the gully, for a kind of trail slants down the embankment. I stay above, contemplating that my grand children are waiting for me at the far end of the fence, which has now become a quite adequate, embellished cast iron affair *(such as you'd see around a city park – and such as I had in front of part of my house in Franklin)*.

My companion, has come back up, and we're back at the corner of the streets. He tells me he can't wait to see the kids, and goes on ahead of me. I'm half way across the span when he returns and tells me that, having seen them, he doesn't want to any more. I retrace my steps to the corner of the streets. He's gone. Snow has gathered in icy chunks in the configuration of the iron fence, walking along again, I'm kicking it loose and watching it fall into the depths below.

And suddenly I find myself in confusion in some building interior. I've gotten there through high elevations along ocean front vistas. There, though, is chaos. I sense that I'm naked but expecting that Angie and I are going to go somewhere after I defecate in a toilet centered in a room where people are coming and going (the room appears to be like a warehouse employees' lounge area). But I'm back in first realm by the fence by the pit in the ground where Angie appears and is totally off the wall insane, berating me, even while she brings me clothes for my trip. I leave by myself.

1/19/13

I'm in a shopping mall, at least a couple floors high, "balcony" walks along each side of an atrium opening. Stores that border such walkways seem to be housing units. Somehow I drive off in a sports car (that seems a fusion of a Ferrari with a rocket-hood-shaped Tucker. I haven't let anyone know I'm taking the car. As I drive I realize that in such a vehicle the headlights should have gone on along with the engine but haven't. But I manage to locate a switch.

I'm in a hurry to pick up Rich *[my adult son']*. It seems then he's in the car and I'm heading back to get him to a doctor's appointment. The fuel gauge reads empty, but I haven't time to stop.

In a sudden situational shift I find myself in what I assume to be my apartment, but it's vaguely seen as one of the "store areas" of the mall. A couple girls who've been staying there are leaving, but not taking everything with them including a large dog. For a second Casey *[our actual family dog many, many years ago]* is cavorting with this other dog until they knock a little jar of cologne off the end of a shelf and glass shards and smaller pieces sort of shimmer through the air and all over the animals as if they were wet. A couple twenty-ish year old guys appear and are telling me that they have to use my apartment, but that they won't break anything up. They only do that in hotel rooms. *[here, another cognitive fragment from the book on The Who]*.

Again I'm driving the sports car and realizing that I've taken it without permission and when the neighbors in the next "mall-stall" notice it's gone they'll think it was stolen and I may have created a police involvement mess. But I have to get Rich to the doctor's appointment, for some reason to be located in my mall-store apartment.

We're next going up an elevator, arriving at the destination floor. I race down the balcony-corridor, passing the many store-front/dwelling-facades and as I pass neighbor's I notice through the show window that there's some upset activity going on within (no doubt about an assumed stolen car).

But I race next door and into my space. The doctor is there and asks me to accompany him into a rear room where he tells me that he's already had the appointment with Rich. Relieved, I tell him that I have to go back downstairs to return a car.

It would seem the doctor had mentioned something about getting paid, but other than suddenly finding my wallet was absolute priority, there was nothing specific in the dream (such as doctor wanting to get paid then and there). I search the car interior but don't find it.

Suddenly I'm driving the car along a residential street. On one side at one end men are doing grading and landscaping along a water runoff into a brook. At the other end, on the opposite side, a couple guys are installing perhaps 3' diameter, grass-covered pipes as if a wall or hedge at the end of a lawn area. The last of these pieces is an elbow shape which is going to extend the border down to the street level. As I drive by I hear discussion regarding the bend of the elbow being too sharp for it to conform to plumbing codes (designating specifics of bends in order to prevent flow-restriction, for example).

Back in the elevator. Now it seems to be cluttered with chairs and on the floor amid the legs I'm looking and feeling around for my wallet. I come across a couple glasses cases, a key case, ahah!! A wallet – but it isn't mine. It belongs to the owner of the car.

Suddenly my wallet is in my hand *[and I awake palming something else and rather desperate to get to the bathroom to pee]*.

2nd segment – I'm first in an alley or driveway beside a large building, a hedge on the other side from the building. But suddenly I'm amid a large group of people within (I would assume) that building. We're on the second floor which consists of a kind of balcony surrounding an opening (atrium) to the floor below. There's been some kind of affair or event, for the adults are in suits (women's clothing not noted). A few young children kind of race around the balcony.

One of the adults is David Latham *[my former attorney before he retired and his nephew took over the law firm]*. He tells me that we need to settle up on the money. I reply that I don't have my wallet or checkbook with me.

And suddenly again I find myself naked under a blanket, lying on a cot or gurney in an office of the law firm. Maureen *[the long-time law firm office manager]* is there, also *Pat [the long-time office worker at the NEMF trucking where I work – until they replaced her with a temp]*.

I'm somewhat upset, at least conflicted, because Maureen has conveyed to Pat to pass on to my employer that after the following Friday I am going to immediately retire.

1/20/13

From a broad avenue on which I see no houses or other structures, a wide road slopes gently down and ends at some body of water, perhaps the sea, or it could be a river.

On the whole length of one side of this unpaved way there's decking made from heavy wood. It somewhat resembles a dock, but seems, too, made of timbers massive enough that it could be used to support a truck crane or other such heavy construction equipment.

The only problem is that at first it's tipped almost 45 degrees from side to side along its whole length. But as I step on it, it becomes horizontal and also reveals itself to be rotted, the planks flexing to my weight.

I'm next in a yard of a cottage or something. No details are seen. But I leave the property and find myself to be at the foot of the water-ending way and looking up. On the other side of the planking/decking there's a massive depression in the ground. Perhaps there'd been a quarry there, or gravel pit, no longer in operation. I notice a NEMF tractor trailer *[the company I actually work for]* starting to back off the road onto hardly more than a trail that sort of runs back into the regions unseen at the far end of the precipice of the pit.

Noticing that the rear wheels of one side of the trailer are about to roll off the edge I yell, hoping to alert the driver to stop. But I can't make a sound and he continues to back, the wheels now knocking down dirt and rocks and the trailer starting to tip. Beyond any point of return forward, the trailer becomes a weight that pulls the cab up and over the lip and the rig plummets down. At the bottom the whole rig sits upright, rear (now bottom) section of the trailer kind of squished with cab atop.

1/20/13

Night. Outside the house the yard is forest and swamp, dismal, ominous. A psycho or murderer is known to be hiding out in the desolation and dampness. My dog comes into the house and I quickly lock the door.

I find that I'm now in a field and walking with my arm around a slender, attractive girl. She and I are kind of flirting, not quite sexually suggestive, but a bit insinuating mutual attraction. And suddenly there are tables and the field appears to have become the site of a flea market. On the tables and ground beneath them are all kinds of old and antique electric and electronic equipment: movie projectors, radio sets, telephones, appliances, etc.

[that's it!!]

1/21/13

I'm either driving or biking through a dismal city, and find that I must detour from the main street I'm on in order to cross the river. Someone has won a trip on one of the boats that travels the river, and as a bonus he'll be able to actually captain the craft. His boat will be one of a group, kind of a flotilla or regatta. He'll be replacing the usual master of the ship, Captain Conflabulation.

But then I'm in a corridor or hall where long bureaus are against the wall and seem to be used as bars for serving drinks. I'm drinking at one of them, and I'm told that I'm to be a bartender. Aunt Marj *[my aunt with whom I enjoyed dinners and trips until she was in her upper nineties]* . . Aunt Marj wants martinis *[which were her favored drink – and in her nineties it only took a couple sips for her to be slurring her words]*. I'm trying to find the appropriate glasses in which to serve martinis. Wine goblets I'm sure of, but not other glassware protocol.

But then it's to an absolutely chaotic truck garage area *[that seems to belong to the company I actually work for]*. I'm told that after I deliver something locally, I must come back to the garage and drive the sports car I'm looking at to New Jersey. The car resembles a 1950s era Triumph, long hood, open "cockpit", etc. It's light green in color, although in the dream I see no color *[as usual, as far as I can remember except for that one incidence of actually "seeing" the dull, but vivid blue room interior last year]*. I'm already so exhausted that I'm wondering if I'll be able to make it to NJ after I make the delivery (if I'm able to make that).

Ohmygod, I'm now in a warehouse, the interior of which is divided into rooms that are embellished as if in a mansion or castle – and connected, one to the other, by wide double-doors. All kinds of indiscernible stuff is piled here and there, some to the very ceiling, and there's hardly room for me to get by to where I'm, next, being told by someone that an invention to deflect rain off a roof (thus no need for gutters) by means of polarizing water droplets opposite from that of the edge of the roof shingles – won't work. But by bifurcating a concrete surface along its center so that each half forms a plane slanting down from the "ridge" of the division . . . . water will run right off with no problem of buildup.

But I'm back in the crowded rooms and seem to be looking for some particular freight (perhaps to deliver prior to going to NJ in the sports car). The trucking company dispatcher appears, looking almost identical to the minister of the church I went to when I was a kid. I'm telling him that by building shelves all around the perimeter of the rooms, perhaps a couple feet down from the ceilings, all the accumulation could easily be removed from the floors. And he replies that the doors are barred and the windows are boxed-in.

1/23/13

I'm standing on a kind of New Orleans-looking porch that's on the back of a building. It overlooks a very unkempt, scraggly field where my daughter Chris is standing alone until I'm suddenly with her and we're both looking up into the sky where, so high as to be just visible, there's something afloat aloft. After I pass through a major intersection where I've found myself waiting for an extremely long red light to turn, I'm back in the field and I ask Chris if Janine (my niece, Chris's cousin) has come back to earth yet. She tells me that, having called and talked with Janine's mother (who said nothing about Janine being missing), she (Janine) must be back on the ground and safe.

1/24/13

I'm downloading pictures from my computer to my new smart phone. But as I do, the effect is almost like that of "the sorcerer's apprentice". As I transfer a couple pictures, more appear, then more. And I try to slow down the exponential accumulation of pictures, but it seems that even when I delete a picture, its place is taken by two, or three, ...This "tumorous" picture growth seems to reach a point of my being somewhat buried in pictures, then it fades *[as if the dream ends, but without my actually wakening]* – then the whole sequence starts again. *[There seemed to be three sequences of this dream-scenario which came about due to my having been involved in somewhat unsuccessfully transferring pictures to my smart phone for three hours or so before retiring for the evening]*.

1/26/13

I've been called to give an estimate for some kind of construction work. I stand at the top of three little tilted stairs with no railings. Before me is the battered, recessed-panel door on which multiple coats of paint chipped and gouged give the effect of an overview of geological laminations and valleys and plateaus.

Above me the structure rises like a typical three-decker, except that it's a two-family building and where the second floor would be is but blank walls. The third floor is the second floor, but spaced two whole stories above the first floor.

No one is home.

I'm on the phone with some relative from South Carolina *[my paternal relations]* when I'm somehow summoned to another job estimate. Having told the relative to hold on, that with an ear bud I can continue the conversation, I head for the jobsite. It's an immense, old commercial or apartment structure. I meet someone who leads me up over a porch with multiple rotted-out holes in its floor. We enter the building.

The inside is divided up into different areas, in all of which I notice that the floors and walls are brick, angled or arched surfaces, apparently the "back" sides of the masonry in that mortar protrudes from the seams. The overall structural effect is that of being up over the ceiling of a theater, only the ceiling being brick walls.

We pass through a couple of such areas looking at desolation and debris, and descend into lower regions where there are myriad pipes and wires and ducts in confusion and even ruin. I tell whomever I'm with that there will have to be a comprehensive proposal drawn up, specifying just what the work will be, on which a price is to be given.

Across a lawn and then into a building where Angie is at the end of a corridor filled with clothes hanging to dry. I sit on a couch for a moment (the people on the phone from the South having long ago given up and hung up, I realize).

But then I exit a car in which kids (and Angie? And others?) remain to wait for me. They want to watch TV and I go looking for a cord to plug one in. In some basement area where it's pitch black. I'd left a cord there, but someone has taken it. In an upstairs area and behind boxes and a washing machine I don't find a cord.

A young girl, perhaps Chris, is standing in front of me and complaining about spraying.. But others kind of emerge into view as if forming focus of faces and bodies. One of them is a teenage girl, in charge of some kind of evangelical affair in which someone is to "play" the Judas or scape goat as a parade of others go by. It's not meant to be dangerous, she explains, but the "victim" will have to be tolerant of a lot of abuse.

She's holding a big, Xmas-wrapped box that's to be given to the one chosen for the role. She asks a dark-skinned girl if she's a Christian. The girl says no.

Suddenly I realize that this is taking place in one of the areas of that big building with the brick walls and basement pipes..

Jack stands beside me. The girl holds the box out for him to take, asking him if he's Christian. He takes the box, thus will be the "Judas", but he makes no reply to her question. I'm thinking, bemused, that he's a hypocrite, but at least he's got whatever is in the box.

At the two-family/three-story place again. I ring the bell. After a wait, an Hispanic woman pokes her head out of a third-story window on the side of the building. She tells me that the work has already been done, for she never heard from me. I tell her that I was there but there was no answer to the doorbell.

1/27/13

I am upon Main Street (rte 28) in Stoneham on a dismal, rainy night. With me is perhaps my father, although whoever isn't seen. We realize we have to get to Linden (part of Malden, a nearby city) quickly. But for some reason I've parked in front of some building in which we seem to be looking for someone as we walk through new interior construction (doors, drywall and over pieces of Styrofoam insulation).

Next we've gone into the building adjacent to the first. This place is associated with some Catholic church and I notice a big card pinned to a wall which, as I first read it, seems to say "To A Priest And His Daughter".

We're outside on the small parking lot in front of the buildings. The car is gone. I'm thinking that since my new smart phone has "phone-find", the vehicle can be quickly located – except that the phone is in my pocket! I should have had a transponder-system installed in the car.

Next, I'm in a line outside tall buildings as if in a major city-scape. But here, people, a lot of them with little kids and infants, are lined up for some reason and eventually reach a long table on which someone has perched a couple babies with whom I'm making faces. At this table one pays for whatever is the reason for the line-up.

Then I'm inside what seems to be my house. It's going to be sold. I realize that I'll net a significant amount (considering the cost 35 years prior) – but I clearly see, as if for the first time, how stained and faded is the wallpaper in   the room I'm in (a flock intermixed with reflective silver floral configurations), and how patched and cracked the ceiling overhead. But I head for the door to leave before the real estate agent arrives with prospective buyers.

1/30/13

I'm in a field and talking with Kenny *[who was my Franklin next door neighbor's son, probably in his forties when I moved a couple years ago]*. There's no indication of the subject of our discussion, but I'm aware that I'm killing time while I wait for delivery of set of iron spiral stairs. In the dream I picture a section of upright pipe, perhaps eight feet high. Its diameter would be 6 feet or so, except that one third of its surface has been cut away, leaving what can best be termed a "slot" from the top of the pipe to the bottom. Within the pipe, accessed from the "slot" at both top and bottom, steps are welded to the inside surface in typical "spiral stair" manner.

I'm talking with Kenny and waiting for delivery of this pre-fab metal staircase which is to be installed in an already existing excavation in the field!

But suddenly it seems I'm in the house in which I used to live in Franklin. I've been stapling very thin sheets of Styrofoam here and there. But I come to the front corner of the living room and notice I can see through where some of the floor boards are missing. And beside these somewhat ragged punctures of the floor there's a protrusion that's pushing the rug up like a tumor.

I'm in the cellar now, looking up at the underside of the floor, seeing wet strands and shreds of polyethylene film which I pull down.

Suddenly I'm in an unknown, very large room, its floor covered with exceptionally thick shag carpet. I'm carrying something, looking for a place to put it (and, it seems, thus to determine where I'll be sleeping in this room). At one place there's a span of floor-to-ceiling glass. I don't want the exposure. Toward the center of the room there's a large four-sided pilaster which I approach.

1/31/13

A woman is riding a bike or motor scooter on the road in front of me and a toddler drops from her arms and lands on its head.

I'm in a large auto and truck repair facility, in a line to get an inspection done. For some reason this place seems to be in Brockton, MA

On a hillside where a big party setup is taking place, for one thing to celebrate my getting a sticker, but also because my daughter (or someone else's) has achieved something or other. At a concession stand I get a bowl of baked beans with a big chunk of hamburger or meat loaf, and meet a guy as I walk away.

He and I are driving and, car and all, we go right into an apartment which he has shared with Jeff *[an actual acquaintance of mine way back who ran drugs for a living, lived in one of my apartments for awhile, became a truck driver, and died young of Hepatitis]*. We emerge, still in car, out the other side of the building. I'm asking him how long he's known Jeff.

I'm at some auto parts place and have the hood up as I try to find some component I want to purchase some add-on for. Then I'm into the trunk where I have something else wired up – and I'm concerned about spending money.

Back at the inspection station garage, I'm in line outside and there's going to be federal investigation that people are pumping gas illegally, hooking up a separate tube to the funnel they use so that they can bypass some kind of emission control in their cars.

Now with someone else I'm at the edge of a cliff and Jeff's room mate comes up with a wheelbarrow partially full of liquor bottles. He's decided to stop drinking, so all three of us begin throwing the bottles down where they smash below. Almost like a reprise, he's now appeared driving a car and we open the hood and remove bottles which we throw down.

2/1/13   afternoon nap

[Nancy Napoleon is the saleswoman for NEMF, a cultured, stunning, early middle-aged woman. After a couple chance conversations last year, I began giving her copies of my writings every so often].

In my dream she's come up to me, I assume to comment on my latest drop-off of papers in her in-box at work *[my Existential Series section on linguistics]*. But she's talking about something else and suddenly we're embraced and very close to making out while classical music plays. *[she's a supporting member of the Boston Symphony and in other artistic and aesthetic interests we're quite alike].*

I'm almost dreaming a physically sexual experience as we dance while going upstairs, and I tell her that I can control only the cognitive complexes of what's taking place. As for the carnal, probably "control" is an oxymoron at this point of my life and besides, I won't "cheat on Angie".

Then we're apparently in her upper-floor apartment where the music playing is causing something on the walls to resonate along with bass notes *[actually the case in my trailer]*. Another guy is now there and he's soon playing a grand piano on which the keyboard is in a totally wrong position – but then he's removed the top and stood the piano up on its side and he's strumming the strings as if it were a harp.

Nancy's complaining about the "jerk upstairs" who complains about the loud music, but creates his own vibrations and thuds on the floor.

Having left her apartment, I'm with the other guy in a car. We're talking about the sounds of the carburetor (intake air noise?) or whatever is creating the high-pitched, fluctuating sounds. He comments that someone should take the car somewhere and get that tuned.

2/2/13

I'm on a broad landing just behind and below the main floor of a walk-up attic in an old house. I'm with others, perhaps members of some fraternal order, and we're there to use the piled-up scraps and fragments of various fiberglass and sytrofoam and other materials to lay on, thus insulate, the floor. We find that the lower sashes of the two front windows are missing entirely, and this segment of the dream ends as we're trying to stretch black pillows across the openings and snugly fasten them to stay in place.

Next I must be in the lower level of the same building. For there are other old guys, but older than above, and we're joking about penis size and geriatric loss thereof. I'm fishing amid bed clothes or a sleeping bag to find my keys as I dramatically recite about how mine used to be a ziggurat, a towering monument, a spire, a domed steeple towering toward God.

Then, it seems, my first true love *[when I was 17 – she was also my first]* has come up from New Jersey and wants to meet with me. I never see her in the dream, but sense somehow being with her again with until I find myself in my car and in the corridor of some immense office building. The passage stretches on and on and when I go through a door I just come to more corridor – now while on a bike for a bit – but I finally emerge behind the building and again in my car. I turn left and drive across lawn, come to the end of a fence, and turn right to go over a low curb and enter the street.

Now I'm driving along with other college-age people kind of stuffed into the car with me. We're talking about something to do with being Irish and Irish humor. Having come to a park, we've stopped and set up a picnic. An Irish girl with whom I've been flirting, introduces me to her brother, a hefty guy slouched on the ground. The girl tells me what a great joke teller he is. I say I hope he has a great sense of humor, because he's Irish and I'm English . Everyone's snacking and I notice that I've spilled crumbs of this and that all around and hope the others won't think me a slob. The inside of my car is a mess.

A sudden segment of the dream involves some entrepreneurial young woman whose product is "bubble-wrap" containing *holy air* sealed into the bubbles of the packing material. The air may have been sealed-in at Lourdes or the Vatican or Mecca or Jerusalem . . . or wherever. The Holy Bubble Wrap is going to be sold by the square foot as a religious item for veneration, even worship. As well as for packing stuff.

But again I'm in a car and, it seems, driving up a mountain that has some vague association with Mt. Washington in NH. At the top. And I'm heading down, fast, noticing all kinds of writing and other figures and ciphers on the pavement. At the foot of miles of racing downhill this wide (but undivided) highway suddenly ends at an intersection of several streets that all pass between *[vague color actually seen in this dream]* red brick 19th c.era mill and factory buildings which seem endless along the street I've chosen. Interspersed with the factory structures here and there are three and four story townhouses with their high steps and scrolled railings to ornate front entries.

I'm on my way to New Jersey, where that first true love actually lived *[and at 17, to where I made several love-inebriated trips for but brief encounters with her before the "affair" ended, in part due to the distance]*. But in the dream I continue on through the industrial buildings, considering it odd that a major route thru New York City and on to NJ and below, would end, with no signs, at such an intersection of streets leading through such dismal regions of a city.

Eventually I emerge, it seems onto the same lawn from which I exited the office building's corridor earlier. Turn left over the grass and right over curb and, now, I turn left onto the street (earlier, I'd gone right). I come to a light. It changes and I turn right onto a busy thoroughfare. As I accelerate between adjacent decrepit buildings of early 20th century vintage (unimproved – such as repair shops, warehouses, store fronts, etc.), coming the other way a vehicle that resembles an organic monster somehow fused with an naval attack vessel, the mutant composite on "monster-truck" wheels . . . this thing passes me a bit too closely and I'm intrigued by the extent of rust and body rot and other damage and deterioration it reveals.

2/3/13

At the top of narrow stairs there's a pre-trial office. People are leaving, others being held until trial. An official tells me that the holding facility is kept at 20 degress F. I realize there's no way I'd be able to survive in such cold and had better not be in trouble. But for some reason I use my fingernail to carve out a small square through the wall surface until stopped upon reaching a metallic barrier within.

In a sort of canvas car-tent in someone's front lawn I'm naked and showering in preparation for a medical appointment. I move to an attached, but smaller shelter and call Angie. Angie and I are then driving through the theater district, considering how far Rich has come in mechanical and other manual abilities and self-assuredness. We stop for coffee, double-parked, and the waitress gives me a pass to park in a lot a couple door down next to the shoe store. As I leave to park she hands me a complimentary chocolate muffin.

I've passed a barn-like building where it seems I may have been supposed to pick up bricks that I can see stacked in the large doorway that's reached by a ramp.

I've parked in front of a building that seems a haphazard combination of factory and old school building. Part of the area in front of it is on street level, the rest is at least a story-height lower. I'm told I have to move, and as I approach the depressed area it rises and when I park on the other side of the structure I'm on the same level as I was before.

Within the building I climb stairs to find myself at Dr. Moore's office *[my previous doctor in Franklin]*. He's done an appendectomy on me and we mention his bill ($750.00) which I tell him I don't have with me as small change.

One of my teenage grand sons *[he's now 20]* is telling me about one of the latest fads: kids are dressing in spandex diapers, consuming laxatives and devouring fiber and bulk edibles, and suffering extensive immersion in their vile feces even to the

point of their skin being eaten away and huge pustules erupting like tumors . . . . the reason being to experience ultimate sexuality.
through suffering. As he's telling me, I notice magnificent yachts moored just outside the plate glass wall.

2/4/13

A mere flicker of a dream of driving along a highway and just ahead of me a deer and then in ibex dart across the way.

2/5/13

I driving cross-country to son Jack's in San Diego. I have as passengers two girls who are paying me to take them. On arrival at Jack's I explain the presence of the unexpected "guests" who are with me and don't seem to have anywhere else to go in San Diego.

I observe Jack and Rich fighting, then tumbling down the stairs to the family room level, where Jack hits his head on the wheel of a car parked therein. But he's alright and seems amused.

Next I'm taking Jack's wife, Laura to work, but because we don't know the right route, I pull into what I think is a gas station. But it's a factory where six foot tall barbeque devices are made, their burner chambers attached to the otherwise tall cabinet-like configurations like backpacks. One of them starts to tip over, and it's only with difficulty and others' help that it doesn't crash to the ground.

South of the city I find myself in a luxury limousine with Dale *[one of the truck drivers at work] and* looking out a fancy window at working-class bungalow-type houses, close-set, repetitive.

Back at Jack's house, he and Rich are again wrestling on a sofa. One of the girls I've brought with me has to leave so she can get to an apartment in San Francisco. Assuming that I'll leave to provide the transportation, Laura's upset that I'll miss dinner. On the road toward San Francisco, I come to a 5-way intersection. The pavements are narrow 2-lane cement, the five streets kind of irregularly spoking out into the different directions, one especially going uphill and curving. I consult my phone's map/GPS AP and choose the latter street on which to continue.

2/7/13

A vague "first act dream" – something having to do with someone on the next peninsula having a fair or carnival. And (perhaps for competition or just as a work of art or satire, I'd created my own fair or carnival out of a combination of *papier mache*. The problem situation was due to the disintegration of my creation which ended up as litter blown all over the actual fair property.

There next seemed an interval of dreaming that I was dreaming at a level beneath even the "unconsciousness" of my dream-state. There seemed an awareness, somehow, of vast and complex neural activity, but it was not on the level of even dream-cognition.

But then I was with someone, perhaps grand son Vin, and we were behind either an abandoned airport or industrial complex on the other side of a very high chain link fence. We looked at a derelict building, either a hanger or warehouse, then turned to see, on our side of the fence, some immense object which could have either been machinery or the remains of a ship. But then, within a building where industrial activity was going on and I passed a Coke machine, I found myself on a wooden freight dock, observing that a large machine fastened to a sledge made of heavy, antique timbers, had been cleverly fastened inside a fairly new metallic box (kind of like a truck body).

[some of this latter imagery was the "combipretation" of info I'd seen concerning salvage operations to be conducted on that sunken cruise ship – and a frequent freight delivery location in Ayer, MA.]

2/11/13

I emerge from a plate-glass fronted store onto a very busy main street of some city. I cross the street in order to get to an appointment with someone in a building on the other side. But I'm not sure which building, remembering only what the inside of the upstairs waiting room looked like.

Across the street, I enter a store-front, find a corridor leading toward the back, expecting it to take me to an elevator. But I end up at a tiny, cluttered office where a rather startled man looks up and asks what I'm doing there. I explain my search for an elevator. He advises I try another building.

But then I'm crossing a field on which a team of young women are stark naked and playing some sport. I gaze upon the exquisite beauty of one especially.

Suddenly there's no more field and I'm behind the wheel of my tractor-trailer rig and rain is a deluge and my windshield wipers get tangled with each other (kind of like when typewriter striker-bars would get crossed and stuck). I pull into a somewhat flooded back lot behind what could be the desolate, brick buildings of an old mental institution. From the pavement I can't reach the wipers, so I unlatch the hood, pull it up and forward, and expect it to "latch". But it slowly seems to fold into two parts and descend to the ground.

Wet, wondering how I'll ever get it back up, I'm climbing the tilted stairs in a very narrow tenement stairwell and suddenly find myself in the apartment of an elderly woman. No details of the place or the person are evident at all.

But I'm back crossing from the tenement to where the truck is, hoping that I haven't been blocking any access to any unseen freight doors. Balancing along a beam, I notice that on one side the rain water is only inches deep, on the other it might drop off to abysmal depths. But I reach the truck. I'm standing in the ankle-deep water. I crouch down and manage to lift the hood back into place with no problem at all.

Whether I first untangled the wipers was not evident in the dream.

2/15/13

First I'm in a huge field of varying, but gradual, topography. With me are two mongrel dogs and we're cavorting over the slopes in euphoria. But then the broad expanse constricts as if we approach a bridge in Venice. On one side of the bridge there's chain link fence. One dog scurries under it, the other one climbs up and over, and both topple below.

Below seems to be a semi-frozen river, but that state makes its transition between liquid (water) and solid (ice) actually a frigid, flowing gelatin. Into this substance the dogs sink, their mouths gaping, eyes hollowed, the whole apparition horrifying.

At first I fear they're lost, but then someone else and I are on a trail through woods and we come upon the dogs, shivering violently, and huddled together. The other man takes one dog, I one, and we cuddle then within our cloaks to warm and comfort them. The one I hold smiles up at me.

Then there's a car, 1950s vintage, with an animal that could be a baby rhinoceros somewhat tied over part of the trunk and a rear fender. But it falls off and lands on the ground in a puff of dust.

And then in front of some building. On the cement walk, surrounded by pools and piles and spews of emesis and other body wastes are various species of creatures, flat on their backs, their legs splayed. Whether they're dead or just deathly ill is not discernable.

And finally I find myself standing behind my rig. I was delivering heavy construction materials to a job-site where there was no dock. I had no pallet jack, so no way to get the freight to the rear of the trailer for a ground-level fork lift to take it off. But as I again look into the trailer I see something flitting to and fro, picking up a pallet at a time with a protruding arm that resembles that of a backhoe. *[The machine is also in the configuration of the smallest rental backhoes, an actual construction device, but almost as cute as a toy]*. But the way it moves, becoming airborne and zipping back and forth with pallets, it seems more to be a fusion of a flying saucer and a house fly!! But it is getting the freight to the rear of the trailer and I watch, amazed at how it floats and zigs and zags through the air.

2/16/13

I'm at son Greg's gated house. He and Tina and the boys leave me to watch the house, there in that affluent neighborhood. From the front lawn where I've watched them depart, I enter the house, frightening their dog with my unfamiliar presence.

But suddenly I'm crossing the street from their house, and across that street is a row of three-story tenement-like buildings, entries to upstairs apartments interspersed with shops on the street level. I enter a narrow corridor, having heard people talking about guy having been convicted of some crime involving a child. Exiting the corridor I'm in a backyard with plush lawn cloaking a knoll on which a man and a little girl are involved in tricycle training or something, and something's said by someone about the convicted man having deserved whatever will afflict him for the rest of his life.

And suddenly I'm with Greg and we're on the way North in separate vehicles. I was making a planned trip, but he's decided at the last moment to extend his vacation time. We find ourselves at the top of a long, long highway hill. There, at a kind of cul de sac, various stores form a haphazard shopping center that's quite busy with people going in and out of the shops. Greg and I sit on a lawn and he toys with the dials of a suitcase-sized portable radio of 1930s vintage, it seems.

When he disappears from the dream, I'm still there with the radio, and realizing that I'm probably as far North as Presque Isle, Maine.

2/17/13

A car repair company. Located under upstairs apartments, its two garage doors open off a narrow alley. In back there's a small lot where a couple luxurious motorized campers are crowded-in. I consider how either of them would be so much more comfortable than the pickup truck I sleep in during the week. But I return to the garage doors to find out if the proprietor has finished whatever with, it seems, Angie's car. He has. I pass him some documents and say that I assume he keeps files on his customers. He says yes, and takes the folder and places it in an antique, two-drawer, oak file cabinet.

Angie and I enter the parking area of a mall on the opposite side from where we usually park. She gets out of the car and starts walking toward the mall ahead of me. She falls. As I approach, a couple are supporting her between them. They tell me she's hurt her leg. Angie tells me she can't go shopping.

Dressed in suit and tie, I'm with several other men on the lower floor of a house *[somewhat resembling Jack's mother-in-law's house].* We seem to be waiting for Laura and other women to arrive. Jack appears on an upstairs balcony and as I look up, I wonder why there's a piece of crown molding nailed at such a deviant angle from where the wall and ceiling meet. Jack starts down the stairs but suddenly jumps the whole floor-height and lands loudly. He and I and unseen others then seem to be on a moving porch that could also be a parade float. He passes me a financial statement designating $21,000.00 on a bottom line and we begin to move along.

Next I'm walking on a broad back street behind commercial buildings seen only on one side. Ahead there are one-story industrial shed-like buildings. Around and against these structures are piles of construction waste materials: fragments of particle board, scraps of sheetrock, distorted metal framing, broken-off studs and joists, etc. etc. Amidst this mess, up on a sort of revolving pedestal, is a mint-condition, 1960s or so VW beetle. As I walk and dream I'm pondering the meaning of such a dream, I hear announcements being made as if on a public address system. The police department is notifying various people by name of offenses pending against them and that they should promptly get down to the station to take care of the matters.

2/19/13

First I'm in a vacant warehouse, thinking "thank God they moved out."

Next I'm in an occupied factory where a guy's railing at a politically liberal woman, possibly a reporter. His tirade seems to be about her anti-war stance that is an affront to his experience of combat injuries in WW II or Korea.

Then I find myself in an upstairs room, at a table, next to my father to whom I'm complaining about a second time of his putting ashes into my tea.

And then a view down onto a deck over which someone carries a miniature antique-style grade-school desk with attached chair. The object seems to be woven from wicker such as would be used for rustic porch furniture. The person is passing it through a window to someone as a gift. Someone behind me is commenting about it being a really stingy gift, but I see it as unique, perhaps even valuable. I say nothing.

2/20/13

I seem to be in an Inuit village where, I'm told, the people keep baby seals as kittens . . . . until the animals are old enough and they're held immobile and their brains are sucked out and they're used for bait to catch other animals.

Next a high-elevation area, an abrupt drop-off on one side which I'm annoyed that Rich hasn't contoured into a slope (rather than cliff) as he and I had discussed. But in trying to express my displeasure I'm talking about smart phones and music APS with several twenty-ish-aged guys. *[My smart phone had self-shut-down during the evening, perhaps due to my reaching a data limit streaming music (that I thought I was picking up off WiFi – but wasn't].*

2/21/13

I'm in an open-top sports car with unseen others, Angie perhaps driving it and lurching as if racing. We're heading for the distant John Hancock Tower which we finally approach the top of as if from the outside, and over a rising road that resembles the back way up to the Leominster Best Buy plaza. Just about at the summit I look over and see a man perched on a chain link fence that surrounds the top of the next skyscraper and I mention that I hope the hell he has several safety ropes in case he falls.

We are suddenly descending within the building. A continuous corkscrew ramp with no vehicular access to intermediate floors finally brings us almost all the way down – at which point the vehicle is a bus and I observe that the driver's side rear view mirror is but a fraction of an inch from the ramp's curving wall and appreciate the bus driver's skill.

We then pass through a large area that resembles a discount store interior.

With former Franklin neighbors Ron and Mamie in their house and Mamie is complaining that Rudy (one of their close friends) had come by, it seems not to visit, but to try to acquire money due to some injury or other that was causing him great pain in his arms. Mamie relates telling him that she can't alleviate the discomfort and won't give him money that she doesn't have.

And then I've been listening to a short dissertation about some scientific matter on the radio prior to finding myself sitting on the opposite side of a conference table from a Haitian woman, apparently a scientist. We're discussing how dangerous it is (using Thalidomide as our reference example) for insufficiently researched (thus assumed) efficacy to be promoted and marketed (as "proven") remediation, especially cure. *[dreaming, I realized that this all had to do with the digital clock given to me by one of the dark-skinned warehouse guys at work – that seems keeps accurate time but of which the alarm doesn't work!!]*

2/22/13

A stark corridor in some kind of institutional building where an unseen, but known to be professional, man picks up a cat off the floor and with a knife almost slices the poor thing's lips off. He hands the cat to me along with the knife and scissors and instructs me to finish the amputation.

Horrified, I cuddle and try to console the animal until I pass a mirror and see that I hold nothing and that reflected is my face upon which there's absolutely no mouth at all, just a swath of skin from eyes down to chin (a slight resemblance to looking at my torso!!)

I'm next in a VW beetle and I stop to pick up a young guy who's soon showing me pictures of a car he's customizing, but hasn't yet got on the road. So I agree to drive him home and we head on down the dark roads through vague areas until we reach a city where I stop to inquire where we are. It's Rockland, about 30 miles south of Boston. My passenger informs me for the first time that he lives in Manchester, about 30 miles north of Boston.

Somehow to find the route to Manchester, he and I are seated at a table, apparently in an executive-level cafeteria. With us are a number of young, attractive women dressed in business clothes. A couple of them get up to leave, but first consult with another pair, sitting with the guy and me, about the best route to Manchester. One of those still seated logs onto Mapquest on the computer in front of her.

Suddenly it seems I'm alone in a different corridor of a different institutional building, this place set on high, contoured cliffs descending to an unseen ocean. I seem to be waiting for something, and eventually knock, then open a door to a room where several professional-looking men are conferring. One of them tells me to wait outside, he'll be right with me.

I wait, then realize that I have to move a temporary barrier warning of a wet floor (being washed) if I'm going to be able to open the door to leave the building.

2/23/13

The young, lovely sales woman at work has invited me into what seems to be her bedroom. She stretches out and, almost naked, shows me a tattoo very high on her inner thigh. It consists of three lines of small print – some quotation or other. She's quite impressed that I notice that one of the words, "exception", is misspelled ("ecception"). I start to touch her but she's suddenly up and gone.

And I find myself with a crowd of people in a gondola ascending an extremely steep cable to some summit. The elevation of the car ceases due to mechanical malfunction, but everyone within who can reach has grasped the cable and we're all pulling it on up kind of "hand-over-hand". I worry about metallic splinters and especially at one point at getting my fingers caught where a spring extends (making spaces between the coils) and then retracts.

At the summit there's a large park where all the people are gathered, some sitting, some standing, all, it seems waiting to partake of a group enema to be administered by the network of tubing all across the plantings and paving.

But suddenly I've exited a building onto a semblance of lower Washington St. in Boston. I'm looking up at the five-or-so story height theater façade across the street, noting its resemblance to the (now) Opera House as if fused with some archeological ruins in Turkey. I realize how desecrated is the locale, and that nothing is being performed there any more.

(Finally we have here a dream that could be easily subject to Freudian analysis!!!)

2/24/13   Afternoon nap

Rich and I are in cab of NEMF rig returning from somewhere, and just having started from being delayed by something. Traffic clears ahead and we start off, and just at a bend in the road become aware that law enforcement is behind us signaling us to stop. I worry for a moment if it's the Saudi religious police.

I exit the cab and walk on the traffic side to the rear of the trailer where someone tells me that the cop is walking towards the cab on the other side of the trailer. I catch up with a state cop, very friendly guy, who points out that the distance between the cab and trailer is almost nonexistent. I inform him that I didn't arrange it thus, that it was already hooked up when I embarked on my trip.

We enter a building, pass through what seems to be a vacant dining room, and take a seat in the rear portion of what has a bus attached like a protrusion from the building. There, we conduct some kind of paper exchange or discussion (not detailed in the dream). Finished, I notice how strewn with trash the floor is, including right where we're sitting, a large slice of tomato.

But the tomato is then in a sandwich I'm eating as we approach the exit from the building. At that point I'm just about to ask the cop why drivers of buses don't get stopped for speeding and operating in the restricted high-speed lanes. But he's preoccupied with what seems to be the opening through the wall into a shaft to the dumpster.

[Fascinating, a couple days after this dream there was an article in the Boston Herald ..." Federal records show nearly a third of licensed bus and limo firms in the Bay State are operating under closer federal scrutiny because of violations . . . ". "Inspection records from the Federal Motor Carrier Safety Administration show that of the Bay State's 89 federal licensees, 29 either were slapped with a serious safety violation in the last year or failed to meet certain benchmarks during inspections." The article goes on specifying operating over 15 mph in excess of speed limits for several carriers, as well as for a couple, drivers without commercial licenses and for one, drivers who could speak no English. Hmmm? Was my dream somewhat premonitory?]

2/26/13

I'm trying to get a long screw to go straight into the forehead of the manager of the trucking terminal. I'm using a sheetrock screw gun.

Suddenly I'm going up a narrow set of tenement building stairs and I come to a crowded room where some of the people are my unrecognized inlaws. There's consternation that people are missing from the gathering so with others I begin tearing boards from the floor which, for some reason is waist-high. Stuffed between joists we find the naked bodies of Terri and a couple other adult women, then closer to the outside wall, infants which to our relief after initial horror and shock, are found to be just very realistic rubberized dolls.

Then the room I'm in is a penthouse that resembles a streetcar interior. I'm sitting with others at a banquet table. Each of us has a punch bowl. The host is complaining about the beverage, which he fears may be gasoline. I inform him that he should have added strawberry ice cream instead of vanilla.

The last segment of this night's analysis-defying dreams: I'm at a candy counter, holding what is the color and size of a plastic garbage bag. As I try to place a handful of liquorice bears in it, the sack congeals in a manner suggesting extreme static cling . . .but also a defensive maneuver of some octopus-like marine creature. It re-configures as a sack when I move my hand away. But to a handful of gum drops it congeals even more, actually to but a crumpled plastic nodule. I move my hand, it "reinflates" itself. Frustrated, I turn to someone unseen beside me who tells me that I should know enough to feed it jelly beans.

2/28/13

In an old mansion and I traverse a hallway, pass wide opening to what seems like a dining room, and come to a doorway. I open, enter, and there at a table is my (former) attorney Joshua Latham. He's with F. Lee Bailey and another unseen attorney. F. Lee's playing some vocal music and perhaps some video as well on for Joshua on his smart phone. Josh seems annoyed.

On a pad of paper I jot three items: past unpaids, closing costs, and retainer for the present year. I hand the pad to Josh, designating that he should just jot down the amounts concerned. I apologize for the terrible handwriting, explaining that I just can't write decently when I'm standing.

Josh gets up from the table and hurries out of the room. I leave right behind him and follow him but don't enter the room into which he's gone.

3/1/13

A parking lot that slopes off on one side overlooking a valley. Surrounding it otherwise are tall, blank brick walls of tall buildings. I leave that area with some others and we seem to be in some part of Mexico, off on a diminishing road until underbrush encroaches and obscures the view ahead. We're heading for some ruins, possibly of a zoo, when one of the group is enveloped by a swarm of something or other and then he and it disappear.

We decide against continuing and get a ride in the back of someone's pickup truck. Back at the parking area I'm in a car and need to fill the gas tank before heading on homeward. There are gas pumps now at the edge of the lot, and I wait in line.

Howie Strathie *[a friend from back in college]* is operating a little drone which resembles an oversized lady-bug, pure white. It lands first on my nose, and I shoo it a way, but then it's on me again and suddenly it opens up like a laptop. But there's double-print on the screen so I can't read it and look above where some kind of creature is climbing around in the tall tree. When I look back to the drone it's turned into a plump piglet that's slobbering me like a puppy and seeking my affection. I cuddle it, concerned that it might fall backward off the boulder on which we're perched.

Along a road, elevated above one side of which are long rear facades of either castle-like or mansion-ish buildings. When I reach a driveway that takes me abruptly uphill to the fronts of these buildings, I realize they're a parochial school complex. The main floor is a floor-level above, thus where I find myself is underneath a kind of balcony that fronts the whole stretch of structures far into the distance. It resembles being under a highway ramp.

Suddenly I'm inside somewhere where it's being explained to one of the drivers at work that by learning mechanical repair technology an income far surpassing truck-driving can be made. And for that purpose I have in hand a sort of stool-like contraption made out of wood that needs to be repaired so that it can be used for mechanical technology employment. I find myself descending into a basement area of the above parochial buildings where workmen are carrying out demolition debris. Locating a foreman, I show him the thing I'm carrying. He's aware that someone would be bringing it.

And finally, with it (I assume repaired) I'm at a stoplight and all but under a truck's trailer in my little car. I wait for the green so I can return to the parking lot with the gas pumps.

3/2/13

[I haven't mentioned this before, but it's the typical "re-mergence" of dream content that I experience. Though occasionally I'll awake with instant and complete memory of what I've dreamt, most of the time I awake with full realization of having dreamt somewhat epic expanses and extents, but only partial or segmented recall of the image-sequences/collages, kaleidoscopes.. But, similar to when a "dozing" computer is activated, the imagery (including some emotional ambience) kind of congeals onto the screen of my wakened consciousness. . . . and thecomplete program of my sleeping unconscious is played-back. And so it was this morning, 3/2/13, at about 7:30 AM when I awoke.]

First I was in what seemed to be a restaurant, its tables and chairs (some with benches) located on a rather steeply sloping floor upwards to the rear. It was as if a theater balcony's seats had been replaced by restaurant furniture. At the very rear (and top) of the place a counter ran across where I used my work time-card to punch-in. Someone there notified me that the dispatcher *[of the trucking company I work for]* was looking for me.

I find Ron at the very front of the place. He and I discuss whether I want to take a load of Motorola or of leather, the latter extremely heavy. We come to no decision when I'm again on the upper part of the slope and a counter is on one side. I'm unable to find my time-card to punch-in and as I discuss the problem with someone, I realize that I'd dropped my wallet the evening before and the card must have fallen out.

Behind one and surrounded by a couple other partially destroyed brick school buildings I'm amid frenzied children and terrified teachers as bombs fall.

But in a kind of alcove or alleyway behind (or within) very old and decrepit one-story industrial buildings I'm walking up a very cracked ramp that was obviously poured and roughly contoured some years before. It leads from the ground level to garage doors into the buildings. Those doors are shut and I find entry via a pedestrian door to one side.

But back at the sloping restaurant, I'm on the opposite side now and choosing a couple sugared donuts from a box on a table. When I reach the upper rear counter, a black man inquires what my coffee preference is and I tell him French vanilla.

Where I next find myself somewhat resembles a very dismal Newbury Street in Boston. The row-town-houses' first floors are commercial or professional spaces, and some of the buildings have excavations that allow access into basement stores or offices. I'm looking for a place that's concerned with my truck driving, but have walked into an office of an anemia organization. A woman at the reception desk advises that I need to go a few doors down.

There, at the foot of a half-story staircase, a little alcove opens off the landing. In it, the very tall sales manager *[of my trucking-job terminal]* is using a urinal. We exchange greeting and I descend the rest of the way. I'm suddenly confronted by a Caribbean man who's very upset that his and other minority people live in areas and circumstances of deprivation and degradation in an otherwise elite and impressive city – Boston.

I reply with a veritable diatribe about the almost exponential disproportion that allows so many so much that they have to stuff it in the ever-proliferating Public Storage facilities . . . while others don't even have a swimming pool to set amid the trash, condoms, and discarded syringes (and bullets) of their neighborhoods.

Ron *[dispatecher]* has appeared again and he and the Caribbean man are talking about a movie. The latter starts describing a scene. Ron interjects to continue the description. Both are joyous that they've shared seeing the movie and they embrace, even cheek-kiss each other. I look on with bemusement.

But then I'm out on that street again and I'm looking for the entry of before, pass the anemia façade, go on a bit. Parked are a couple interesting vehicles, one of which turns into a gigantic, somewhat mangled, truck that seems to be in a very distorted reiteration of the alcove-and-cement-ramp area.

3/3/13

A crowded corridor in either a hotel or office building.

From a lower level, a set of bulkhead doors fly open and Richard comes charging up to where I am. He has a pistol in a paper bag. He wants me to carry it.

In a car, I in the back seat still refusing to take possession of the gun.

On a flat, dirt, vacant lot where buildings have been torn down (it seems) on the East side of Main St., Melrose, I lay.

Within someone's house I'm looking for ear plugs. I'm going to have to cut metal with a skill saw, in order for a Comcast service man to be able to secure satellite dishes connected with intricate framework, the whole assembly to be
able to roll on a track – to the top of his van. I can't find the ear plugs.\

I'm driving at night up a steep hill with forested drop-off on one side and expensive houses on the other. I hear an elderly woman's voice and realize that she and others might be able to use the step-stool, little two-wheel grocery cart, and a bicycle that I have with me. I've taken them out of my car, but before I can leave, a woman from one of the houses across the street somewhat accosts me, but becomes more friendly when I explain that I'm not just disposing of junk. She and I end up in the lower level of the barn attached to her house where a young boy cuddles up with her.

But I continue on up the hill to the impressive domicile at the summit where I explain various aspects of all the above to whoever the people there are. And I realize that I must leave to get back to the poor Comcast guy who's been waiting for me to cut the metal. I descend the stairs to where my car's parked, but can't find my upright vacuum cleaner. A little girl searches here and there as do I, including over a wall where the view out over a vast valley is quite remarkably a replica of a vista in the movie, The Lion King.

    Down the snowy hill I go. I stop. On each of three trees where little stubs of broken-off branches make "hooks", I hang the bike, cart, and stool.

3/4/13

    I'm standing at a counter which is located in the center of a truck-repair garage. Around are commercial vehicles and strew. Behind the counter there's one of the drivers from work to whom I pass a rod of some kind.

    I walk around to the right of the counter and into the back part of the area and find that there's no access to the restrooms from that side. I have to go all the way back around the counter and to the right rear.

    In the narrow, dingy hallway I walk, noting that the walls seem to be cardboard and would really look nice if painted blue, or maybe even rose color to provide more "ambient illumination" to the area. Through the walls are several openings, a couple into toilet areas. I actually picture myself painting the walls, swath-by-swath, with an airless sprayer, but though I know I'm spraying blue, I as usual in dreams, see no actual color.

    I'm on a road from somewhere I'm unfamiliar with, but which seems to be on a hillside above a river or ocean bay. I descend a bit and turn onto a kind of old state highway which goes steeply uphill. The vehicle I'm driving is the l959 Oldsmobile I owned way, way back. I roar up the hill ahead of other cars coming along behind me.

    I'm in what could be described as a resort-area high-end art and gift shop and gallery. With my daughter-in-law Laura I'm walking around in the bright interior of the building where canvases and linens are stretched on frames atop primarily glass counters and display cases. The fabrics are painted, abstract or oriental or even psychedelic motifs primarily, but in some the pigments have been mixed with granules of sand or mica or metallics so that the images are semi-three-dimensional and *[color unseen but sensed]* strikingly multi-chromatic.

    Laura and I look at a couple of the small, interpretive pieces of furniture on display and I excuse myself and look for a men's room. A young man, perhaps docent or even manager, approaches me and directs me to a paneled door, having determined that my need is only for urination. But just as I'm about to enter, another man rushes by me, obviously in dire need to do more than pee.

    Then I'm standing with the young man in a hallway. He tells me that they're going to put on an addition and, appraised of construction work that I've done, they'd like me to present a proposal and price. I thank him for considering me, but explain that at my age and considering other aspects of my position in life, I'd be ill-advised to become involved with such a project for such an elite enterprise – and they'd be ill-advised to have me. Rather, they should solicit perhaps a half-dozen bids, probably including the company that built the original building and, more recently, a competitor's job *[I seem to have gone past this place in the dream but without realizing it]* just down the street, a magnificent architectural fusion of modern and Greco-classical features.

Having, so to speak, reciprocated being "honored" by my integrity's response to their "honoring" me by asking my participation in their project, we look together at some unseen paintings on the walls as we wait for me to be able to take a wicked piss.

3/7/13

I climb a narrow stairway. At the top I find myself sitting across a desk from my boss. But he looks identical to Kelsey Grammar *[the actor most known for his "Frasier" role on TV]*.

I'm next on a broad dirt "apron" in front of an almost derelict-looking one story garage or warehouse building. I venture to look inside and see only remnants of this or that, probably equipment or vehicles. Otherwise the place looks empty, so I return outside and walk to the side where the surface drops off into a drainage ditch. Rising from it and forming a curving wall for the entry from the road to the garage is a wall, the individual stones hewn to fit so perfectly that it seems like a mosaic.

The broad surface I'm on next is like a derelict deck, as if partially rotted planks had been laid out edge-too-edge on the ground. The planks surround a central space that's like a mud-hole. Next to it, leaning against a door frame that seems to be standing alone, is a woman who vaguely resembles Angie. She's holding a dog and when I approach and kind of lean down, the dog is all over my face with its tongue, slobbering affection on me.

I need to urinate, thinking even as I dream, that the dog's copious saliva may be the "power of suggestion", but then again, perhaps my actual need to take a leak was functioning as the stimulus for the dream!!!

I awake, obviously in need of emptying my bladder.

3/8/13

At first I'm as if on a mountaintop. The distance is an indistinct panorama, Five roads have come together like spokes where I am. One of those roads leads to another such intersection a bit below. From there, I choose from the roads one that seems to be a service path beside a railroad track that goes steeply downhill. But as I start on that route I realize that a truck that seems to be loaded with hay is coming toward me. I cross the tracks and continue on down on the path on that side.

At the bottom I'm driving a kind of fusion of a motor home (such as Winnebago) and the old cab-over truck tractor I used to own. I come to a cluttered repair facility partially built into the hillside. The workers are on break so I wander through the place a bit, passing through a cafeteria and then entering a huge, commercial kitchen where various bowls and glasses and dishes and otherwise of fruit cocktail are covering every surface.

I've driven into the garage repair bay and, along with mechanics, I'm noticing that some bolt threads are stripped (the nuts can be turned by hand), and other faults and failures of my vehicle. But then I'm told that the spoiler
(airfoil below front bumper) has been secured so I'm all set to go.

And I find myself in what seems to be South Boston. Through the narrow streets I'm maneuvering a 53' trailer to make a delivery, but at first can't find a place to stop at the site. I circle a block, arousing the good-natured scolding of a cop, and back at the location manage to pull into a hole in a side of one of the buildings. All appear like Southie tenements, 3 stories high. I climb up the stairway just a to peek at what's above, while, presumably, the freight is being unloaded (or highjacked) from my truck.

I'm back at the trucking terminal which, in the dream, is built on a sloping field. There are three long, low buildings separated by paved areas wide enough to park trailers perpendicular to the buildings. As I walk toward one of the buildings I wave to the terminal manager, George. He's also walking toward the same building as I, in the company of one of the Hispanic drivers. George is telling the guy that he's had a suitable trumpet-shaped inscription done on his grave stone.

Inside the building I start to organize and finalize my paperwork for the day's deliveries and pickups etc. But someone keeps jumbling them from a table, and I end up having to use the floor-grid behind the truck's cab as a desk. But the papers are so many that they keep slumping from the stack. And before I can reorganize, someone has taken my tractor while I've taken a leak.

Searching for my tractor takes me over ridges and down into ravines of an area that may have been a sand and gravel excavation site. I emerge up onto a plateau on the other side. On one side of an old highway I'm in what may have been a skating rink, now abandoned. As I cross to the other side of the road I find myself with others including Joshua *[grand son]* and Charity *[niece]*. A cop has an oncoming car slow down to let my "family group", as well as a Moslem woman wearing chador, cross the street.

Next we're in a take-out restaurant, tables to eat the food on, but just a small, rectangular hole in the wall to the kitchen. There, we start to order what we want, but there's such hilarity and even rough-housing of the cook-staff that we're not getting our orders taken.

From the other side of the street a guy's yelling for me to go back there to get some real Boston food. I find myself at the head of a little half flight of stairs down to a small room. In it several older men are sitting at a table and greet me cordially. As I start down the stairs I sing the first part of the Southie "anthem": "Born down on A Street, brought up on B Street, Southie is my home town . . . . . " The guys are very appreciative, but hasten to tell me that they don't operate a food-service facility there.

And I'm at one of the tables back on the other side. We're waiting for the orders to come out from the little pass-thru to the kitchen. I've finally decided on a tuna melt with chopped onions, which resulted in an uproar of laughter from the cooks.

As we sit, one of the walls of the building becomes transparent and we see Joshua coming. He's in great spirits, having achieved something or other (passing a course? Getting a job? His license?). He joins us and we're all sitting, waiting for our food. But already there are papers *[transplanted from before in the dream when my tractor was taken?]* . . . and containers, and bags, and other objects crowding the table and everything seems to be getting smeared with mustard.

A brief coda (as we still wait) is that Angie (? – or Charity's mother, Patsy?) is very concerned that Charity wants to go make a phone call because it may be her way to escape the group and consort with a male.

3/13/13

Two dogs are running free but there's no scenery, no context. I just know this in my dream.

One dog has two sticks protruding from its mouth like spreading legs of a triangle, the apex of which would be quite deep in its throat, if not all the way into its stomach. In response to a question how that happened, I reply to the unseen questioner that the dog, gulp-by-gulp, swallowed the sticks incrementally.

Perhaps still concerning the dog (or not) I'm discussing a situation with a young woman while doctors are out of sight on the sidelines of what seems to be a steep San Francisco street with ornate, high-staired housings. But we're in front of an opening right off the sidewalk. The woman goes into the building to get towels and hot water.

I realize that she and I will have to do the extractions on the doorstep.

3/15/13 (afternoon nap)
Cutting from top of something downward with a skill saw. I'm close to the young woman who signs out papers at Market Basket warehouse. She may be holding the thing I'm cutting. She seems concerned that I may cut her, perhaps causing some part of her clothing to be removed.

Suddenly in some building and waking to the sound of men working outside the front wall. I go to look at the curved balcony-like room they've added and see that there's been a fire. Seams in the floor have burned to a couple inch width with blackened borders. And, standing on one side, there's the bow-front bureau I used to have. Its drawers are gone and one can see from the smoke stains that the contents were on fire.

I'm in a corridor and my father has asked me why I've mentioned that we may be getting scammed by the addition-builders. I tell him I'll give him details after I take care of personal business. I enter the door beside me and as soon as my truck terminal union steward exits the rest room I enter what looks a bit like a foyer. But up a couple stairs there are two doors. A guy standing at the foot mentions that he also is uncomfortable defecating where anyone might see him, so the second door is preferable.

[I awake, realizing that I haven't yet called-in to trucking company headquarters the information concerning damage to the truck I was driving yesterday. . . . . trucking company shit happens?? . . . . .]

3/16/13
A group of people I'm with. There's no place to park. They're insisting that we therefore have to take multiple vehicles to some event. I protest, pointing out that there are actually many places to park. We only need one vehicle for all of us. Why waste gas?

But I find myself alone in a car and notice that there's a no parking sign where I was going to park. I start to pull in to a yard, the cement drive passing between two little carved granite posts. A decrepit Victorian house stands on the lawn sloping up from the small courtyard that the driveway enters.

Obviously I can park there if I'm working on the house. I'm inside. The place is all but gutted, no doors or frames or baseboards etc, unplastered rocklath not even on all of the interior framing. Upstairs. Up further. Shed dormers have been added to the back of the roof, but the state of structural incompletion (apparently for a long time) is drastic. I can see the sky through crevices and cracks and punctures of the ceiling and walls. I can see down to the ground. For some reason someone has hung sheets as temporary closures to the stairs going down from each of these dormer additions.

I part the fabric as if it were a stage curtain. But before I can descend the stairs, I'm in an office where I'm grabbed by the hair and thrown against a wall by an executive-type middle-aged man. I notice that he looks like an actor in a movie I'd *[actually]* watched prior to going to sleep *[And in the dream I recognize the "componential residue" of actual experience – and that this isn't the first time I've analyzed dream-content in a dream]*.

The guy hasn't hurt me. I observe a reel of garden hose and notice that we're back in the unfinished shed dormer of the desecrated estate house. It's the time, I realize. I tell him, "This relationship isn't working. I can't continue projects started by others."

Any contention thus resolved, it seems, he and I are standing together amiably on the lawn beside where I've parked.

3/18/13

Though going Southward over the Zakim Bridge into Boston on I-93, it seems that I'm going significantly uphill. There are others in the car with me and as we approach someone creeping along in our lane, several of my passengers start shouting invective and slurs and insults. I chide them for their childishness and insensitivity.

And suddenly we're plunging downhill into the Big Dig Tunnel.

And I find myself within a building whose atrium soars up from the ground floor perhaps 15 stories to the very sky-lit ceiling. And suddenly I'm on an upper floor looking dizzily down through the thick glass partition that forms barrier and railing from the balcony-like corridor around the atrium.

At an office I'm made aware that my old fraternity buddy, Howie, and I are going to be launched into an extended stay in space in a NASA rocket.
There's some concern whether we'll be able to coexist in such proximity for such duration – but a greater concern is that of a portly young man in an expensive suit who stands in the doorway, steps aside and joins me as I exit the office. It seems I have some sort of contract or other commitment with the company he represents – entertainment?

In space, I'm alone and swimming through a channel between rectangular planets. I'm approaching an island that resembles a pastry I'd eaten earlier in the day. Closer, I see that I'm not swimming, rather immersed in torrential rain that falls as I stand on a plastic milk crate in order to reach a window on an outside wall of someone's house. I need to shut it so the rain won't get in and soil anything.

Back in the space-swim, I notice traffic on either side of me, but at a distance.

3/22/13

The landscape is a large mound of earth, kind of resembling a parking-lot-sized leech field. I back my tractor-trailer rig up over it, approaching what would be truck dock doors – except as I near I realize they're essentially empty metal shelves. A couple drivers, most clearly visualized being John Doherty *[from work]* are there.

They're in a state of great hilarity, for the freight to be picked up consists of a walrus and a large book known (though not seen) to be pink.

Suddenly Angie and I are driving in a car and after turning at an intersection in the midst of trash and wreckage-strewn vista, we come to be at a parking lot. Richard comes along in a car with others who look like Hispanic gang-bangers. Rich and Angie engage in almost violent verbiage regarding her going to some kind of medical procedure. Richard races off in a rage.

Angie and I are at a house where I intend to unload firewood next to a tree next to the driveway. But in backing the van I'm now driving, I first ram the tree, then pull forward and find I've backed in nowhere near it. Next to me on a rock, a large black cat awakes and I pet it while it savors the attention.

3/23 . . . . 4/3. during this interim, the nightmare of incessant bronchial coughing seems to have taken the place of any dreaming. Several nights I was unable to lie down – had to sit up, yet still cough, unable to sleep. But at least I could breathe. I made it through four work-days, arrived home, and slept for about 30 hours straight. I awoke coughing still. To the doctor. Prescription. I'm better, it seems.]

4/4/13

Several friends from way back in college days are in an older model car with me. We're in a vacant lot beside a run-down variety store, the locale suggesting that the bank in Linden has been replaced by this scenario. We try to back the vehicle close enough to an opening in a wall so that we can look at the engine. Part of the side of the hood opens, like a sliver of a car door, for access to the engine. But it won't open wide enough.

We move the vehicle which is now up to a second-story height beside a building. On that upper floor is a large enough opening for the hood-door to be swung into the building. After positioning the car close enough to the wall, we place a beach umbrella, shovel, crutch, and (I think) tripod in a large sack which one of the guys carries around to back of the building and then up stairs to the second floor.

On the second floor we have to maneuver around various configured racks of clothing as if in a department store. While approaching where the wall-openings are, we're concerned about being apprehended.

At the opening, the objects have been taken from the sack and placed against the wall. One of our group has gone down for coffees and returns very distraught that he's been sexually approached by someone in the variety store. We sympathize.

And suddenly a lobby of an oriental theater is around me, a group of older, very elite-looking women dressed in gowns and wearing gloves gathered around a beautiful young woman who is to perform a highly stylized-unto-perfection vocal work. Suddenly the singer, who has been seated, leaps to her feet (while providing a split-second of ultimate-intimate glimpse of her groin). . . . then the ladies in their finery are acting horrified and petrified. For the girl has ad-libbed and improvised, transforming the ancient ritual act into something abstract and modernistic. From somewhere in the theater a Samurai-like man comes kind of stomping toward the group of women, the older ones berating the singer. They see him, freeze, whisper,

"It's Mr. Smoke!!!", as he waddles forward. He brushes them aside, puts his index finger under the chin of the singer, strokes her hair, and very gruffly tells her (in an accent somehow realized in the dream as a combination of Japanese and of Yul Brinner's King of Siam). . . ."I am pleased with you."

Back at the building we pack put things into the sack and go back downstairs, across a cavernously excavated area behind the building, and approach the car at t he side. It's not back to a regular height.

4/6/13

A big intersection in a run-down section of somewhere. One-story storefronts, one of them the entry for a bar or tavern. Some guys gathered around see me. We know each other from somewhere, and soon I'm being pressured to play piano for the place that evening. After some cajoling on their, and protesting on my, part it's agreed that I shall perform.\

I'm standing on a mezzanine or balcony in what seems to be an almost completed new construction of a massive theater lobby or train station. A glimpse is interspersed as if I'm outside the place, and clearly from what I see in front of what used to be North Station in Boston. But then I'm again on the upper level looking down. It seems that I have some kind of commitment there for the evening.

Suddenly a man in full military uniform is standing below me on the main floor. He's waving a piece of paper at me and I realize that it has to do with my having agreed to play piano at the bar. Ohmygod, I've committed myself to two places at the same time!!

In someone's house where I'm looking for a bathroom, I resolve the problem of my commitments by telling people unseen that I'll just go back and forth between the venues, alternating performance and breaks. I mention that I really should have checked to see just what condition the pianos are in before agreeing to play.

> *[back many years ago my little combo (trumpet, drum, me on piano) was hired to play for a wedding reception. The piano was not only drastically out of tune, but some of the keys didn't strike notes at all. I pretty much faked that I was playing, and hoped that those assembled didn't realize the extent of disaster that I sensed]*

4/11/13

> *[A very early dream was of a huge building, probably an insane asylum, that I entered. Above, I described traversing a corridor which seemed to disappear into oblivion as well as dissolution In the present dream, dreaming as well as later when awake, I'm sure the building I'll describe is the same building – though different. And in this dream, as I dream I'm aware that I've been past this building many times through the years and always been deeply troubled by the place and what it represents].*

The huge, long, desecrated building. I don't see it but know that I approach it, as if through a very crowded neighborhood [picture Sicilian or Greek urban areas on a hill]. There are cats scurrying around. I pass on and have entered an immense building that stretches out before me. I'm in the basement level, the ceiling far above, the walls far apart and the vast space stretching endlessly ahead strewn with remains of materials and equipment and portions of fallen walls and perhaps ceiling too.

Suddenly I find myself outside the ruin, and at the far end from where I entered. I walk down an embankment beside a driveway from the street I reach to a parking lot before the façade of a now quite intact, but still immense, building. The place looks like a massive, fairly modern industrial plant with part of the frontage being office space. I walk up the lawn beside the drive and look through windows at an empty cafeteria, an adjoining exercise room, and beyond, behind neat shrubbery, the expanse of the place on into the distance.

There is no more emotional reaction. There is no more ruin. There is but a structure. I walk back down the lawn toward the street, sensing even before I awake, that this dream represents the end of the emotional trauma that resulted from the end of my first "true love" affair.

But then I've disembarked either an airplane or a bus. I'm In an affluent neighborhood with brick homes set on large lots. Behind the closest I notice there's a church, somewhat like an addition to the house. I'm on a bike!! I ride up over the lawn and back to the side of the church where, down an embankment, I find a way to enter. Inside I ride the bike across a corridor, through a door, and down a flight of stairs. Now in the basement region of the building. A span of concrete ends at a drop-off into what could be described as a foundation. The back wall of it is the back wall of the building.

I look for a way to get down or around, so that I can exit through the door I see on the back wall at the floor level of the pit. I see no stairs or ramp, so step over the edge, holding the bike, and now the pit is full of water and I kind of splash and swim over to a little ladder up onto the original level I'd left – only there's a walkway back to that rear door which is now up at the level I'm at.

I've exited the door and hurry on, riding my bike across a field so that I can get to a restaurant to meet the family for dinner.

4/14/13

I'm on a street in a city. Sees somewhat like Central Square, Cambridge, but no specifics other than multi-story buildings on each side. I park too close to a major intersection and someone and I exit the car and go into a store.

But then I'm with Uncle Billy, Richard Holmes [my old high school friend] and others in a grand entryway to some building. The door we're painting is massive and paneled. The others are applying yellow latex. Billy gives me a tool with which to open my can of paint. But it seems to have gone bad and despite considerable mixing and stirring with my brush, I'm unable to achieve a yellow rather than a streaked green.

On a yacht for a moment.

Back with Billy and others in that entryway. He's concerned that another tenant of the building may have gained entry to his apartment which seems to be upstairs. We explore around the doorways and a kind of equipment closet to one side of the doors, but find no obvious way the suspect (an old guy) could have accessed the upstairs without a key to the door.

And suddenly we're upstairs which is a rather palatial apartment that Bill, his wife Madelaine, and a couple of their daughters occupy. Beds are in every room except one in which a whole crowd of family is gathered around a table. One of the sons and his family arrive from Charlestown and the group is complete. Kim [my niece-in-law, Bill/Madelaine's grand-daughter] holds a little girl with a very chocolate-smudged face and passes her across the table to kiss someone as everyone sings something. But there's the sense of something that's been wrong in that realm and the two resident daughters seem depressed and somber.

And next, with Bill I'm outside and the building with the entryway is now a separate structure like a mansion or municipal edifice. A kind of circular drive fronts it. To one side there's a granite pedestal, about four feet high, atop which is a granite cap (like a table-top) of perhaps sixteen foot diameter (thus overhanging the pedestal by at least three feet all around. The pedestal has a slot, perhaps a foot high, and penetrating into the cylinder by about 1/3 its diameter. Bill and I consider this and mention that the whole assembly might have once been used as a capstan [actually the imagery in the dream derives from the remains of a water-powered horizontal wheel that I'd actually seen when making a delivery to a former textile mill complex in Lawrence, MA – the buildings being converted into housing].

We're going to leave the area, but suddenly the ground is covered with a dry torrent of greenish something and Bill turns away and disappears. Mike [a driver from work] appears and to my mention of something apocalyptic happening to prevent people from leaving the area, he responds that that's the retribution (for something or other that seems to relate to Bill).

I escape the furied flow by entering a ramshackle metal building where some kind of altar with hanging tapestry is on the back wall. But to the cries of a young boy I and others go back out and look down the dirt road where three and four story buildings, some with flat roofs, others with pitches and turrets etc, are standing and suggest a decrepit, degenerate view of Somerville, MA. As we watch and the kid atop one of the buildings screams, all the buildings seem to dis-assemble into geometric fragments of themselves which jostle in place but then kind of tumble into a matrix (like watching a kaleidoscope).

4/18/13

The area I'm driving through resembles Woonsocket, R. I. Others are in the car with me but I don't know who they are. I'm pointing out to them that there's a dam back to the right, and that from it the channels of water we cross, some of which disappear under desolate-looking mill and factory buildings over to the left. And ahead, one of the channels enters a culvert and I explain that it continues on under the street stretching straight ahead. Except for that channel, the others were "races" and the water flowing through them powered machinery in the mills. The one ahead was probably to release overflow from the dammed mill-pond in times of reduced usage or increased precipitation.

Suddenly we're in a back lot filled with automotive and other machinery in various junk stages. There, it seems that I'm delivering rolls of Joistape [tarpaper cut in rolls of 2 or 4 inches and used to protect outside wood construction framing]. With no transition, we're next in a building negotiating to rent a nicely furnished and carpeted two-bedroom basement apartment. I wonder if there'll be enough room for the three of us [which, at that point in the dream, seem to include me and my grandson and his girlfriend].

Outside, the streets resemble Salem, Ma, with various touristy stores. I can't find the car. We look all over, around corners. No car. Finally we call the police and find out that they've had it towed. But due to the circumstances, they shouldn't have and they'll have it returned. And in no time, back in the junk-equipment lot, we watch as a group of gang-banger-like guys bring the (now VW bug) back, unhook it from the tow truck, and race off. I comment that it seems strange that police would operate in such a manner, and it's kind of surmised that a car-theft had been attempted but then, for some reason, aborted.

Heading back to wherever, I'm concerned that I haven't checked the oil in ages and have no idea if there's enough (or any) in the engine. We stop and I add a quart, after which the route resembles the VFW parkway in the vicinity of the VA Hospital in Roslindale, MA. Across that busy road, just ahead of where I'm driving, a toddler kind of sprints. I stop, commenting that a baby shouldn't be alone like that. Right behind him a little boy of 3 or so is running next.

And then two little boys are standing in front of me where I crouch on the median strip of the parkway. Trees tower overhead. The kids want me fasten their jackets, and it seems that they're wearing shoes of which I'm to tie the laces (which close the coats where buttons or zipper would in reality). One kid's coat has little metal clips that the laces just slip behind [like my work boots]. But at the bottom, groin-high, of the other coat, the laces would have to be pulled through button holes. I consider that touching the kid in that area would be unwise, so don't complete his lacing.

And then I'm on a bike.

And a couple dogs run from the lawn beside me, one of them right under the back wheel of the bike. He seems badly hurt and I stop immediately and ask people raking their yard about the owner.

At the designated house I ring the bell and inform a big, professional-looking guy in his thirties what's happened to his dog. We go outside. The dog's nowhere in sight. We consider that we have no idea the extent of injury or even if the dog's gone somewhere and died.

As I'm about to exchange information and leave, the guy seems to resolve the situation by informing me that I'll do some painting inside his house (as atonement or payment or ????) He leads me up an "angularly-winding" rear stairway, on each bend of which there's a panel stretching from head-high up to a lofty ceiling. And each is flaked and needs scraping and painting.

Finally I agree that I'll do the painting, but on my schedule.

Then there's negotiation over who'll pay for the paint. Finally he agrees to.

And then, just before I leave, I tell him that I feel his pain. That I still have latent grief for a dog of long, long ago. He somewhat counters that his grief is an immediate wound and thus not healed like mine. This seems his reason to insist that I take care of the painting sooner than my prior estimate of time-span.

I inform him of my age, that I'm working close to 60 hours a week, and that I just can't do the impossible. And he should realize that having his painting done by me in any time frame would be impossible if I were to overexert and drop dead!!

4//19/13

Another driver and I are each pulling a flatbed trailer loaded high with rolls of insulation. After passing through a vague scenario as if the highway had become a corridor in M.I.T., where we confer with some professor on something, we're back out on the road. We turn off the highway through the entry of a retail store.

Way back in the woods on a dirt road we come to the construction site. A huge barn-like structure is attached to what will be the house. Only the framing is complete, no siding on yet. The side of the barn facing the narrow drive through the underbrush and trees is a vast, gaping space.

I stop, and tie a rope from the front to the back of the trailer in order to secure the load (which, of course, should have been done from the inception of the trip!) Then I pass a coil of rope to the other driver. I drive my rig right into the barn, noting the heavy timber framing in detail overhead – an excellent, mortis and peg job. Close to the back wall the floor level drastically slants upward and as I turn so that the rig is significantly tilted, I consider that this may result in the insulation all toppling off the trailer, thus facilitating unloading.

And then I'm in a food warehouse [to which I actually deliver several times a week]. My son Greg [a cardiologist] is there and needs my advice on what to do with a Comcheck that one of his patients has given him as payment for a procedure. [Comchecks are kind of like Traveler's checks that truckers use to pay for unloading services, fuel, lodging, etc. etc.]. I advise that Greg make a separate folder in his files for comchecks and just keep them in date-sequence. It seems he's not going to be able to cash the one he's been given for some reason.

[afternoon nap] We're standing against a rustic country fence post. A dirt road forks off to one side. Behind me there's a gigantic African guy, probably 400 pounds and standing much taller than I am. As I try to lift a full spare gas can which I've only managed to get waist-high, I lean against him. One of his massive hands helps me raise the can up so that I can hold it over my head and pore into the gas spout that emerges from the top of his right shoulder. Pouring requires that I bend my body over to one side (keeping my arms extended to hold the gas can high enough). Since neither he nor I can see how much gas he's holding, he suggests that we stop the pore for a moment and he'll find something to use as a dip-stick.

4/20/13

A big parking lot with strip-mall stores. I have a load to deliver to one of them. Someone comes up and offers to help me unload, saying that he hopes he's not getting involved in a whole trailer-load of freight scheduled for a new store to be opened at the far end of the lot. I tell him no, I only have a couple pallets for a variety store. In which we suddenly find ourselves being served donuts, and perusing what kind of candy we want.

I've left the store and enter a car where my cousin Jeanne [who was pretty much a recluse until she died a few years ago at 80-something]. Apparently middle-aged, she's concerned about her money, and paying her bills. I advise her to consult with her bank and have bills paid directly, deposits made into her account from whatever source, and disbursements made to her at her request (for whatever specific reason, and in whatever amount she'd designate – subject to the bank's approval).

And then in what resembled a "recombination" of a house I lived in as a boy in Melrose. For some reason I'm naked and have concealed myself in a closet so that one of my sons and his wife won't see me. I hear a kind of trickling sound and look up. Around a pipe coming down from above the roof, water seeps, then drips. I'll have to put roof tar around the pipe, I realize. But suddenly, as if a toilet-flush volume, water pours down. But it's coming through a hatch that leads to the roof. I see the sky above through the hatch. But then I see feet and legs and soon the nude, hips-down length of the teen-age daughter of one of the next door neighbors when I lived in Franklin! I voice my concern and she's pulled back up out of sight.

I'm now downstairs in the house and about to go out through the front door. But to the side I notice that water is pouring through brickwork which appears like the remains of significantly destroyed fireplace and chimney.

In another building, a second floor with a porch all around the outside of the structure. Angie and a scattering of other people are there amid a strew of donuts all over furniture. I'm conflicted as to whether I should dress (apparently being still without apparel) or get my choice of donut before they're all taken. But Angie and I are embraced, kind of making out, and I sense about to experience intimacy and ecstasy such as never before. But as I drive off the front lawn in a 1940s vintage car and look back up at the porch, I only know that Angie is beside me in the front seat.

4/23/13

A hill. Fields stretch out below. A woman who seems to have something to do with the medical profession tells me that I should have my tonsils taken out. I try to tell her that I already have.

In the old GMC truck-tractor I used to own I'm going through city streets and then am parked in a yard. Angie agrees with me that it's in too bad a condition to make another road trip. She asks if I want to go back into carpentry. I only respond that I hope the truck makes it to the junk yard.

Rich and I are together and he needs some kind of medicine. The medical woman reappears. I look beyond her and point out to Rich the foot-long snail that's crawling over the top of a large boulder. Suddenly a much smaller thing (a slug?) that should just ooze along, almost scoots up and over the rock past the snail.

4/24/13

I'm driving with grandsons Nick and Vinnie with me. Their ages suggest this would be about 12 years ago. We seem to be on a back road in Maine, going through a small town where I've been before. But what had been a little antique and junque store, the building has now been enlarged several stories high. We stop, enter, and amid all kinds of heavy construction equipment and noise find out that the place is being turned into a metal fabricating factory.

We go on up the road, around bends, off the pavement, over a hillside field, down a rounded ledge, and back on the road. There, to one side behind a massive entryway that resembles the *Arc de Triomphe,* I point out to the boys the distant, sprawling wall-enclosed buildings of the Maine State Prison. On the other side of the road is a college or hospital campus.

Driving on, I want to show them the huge, haunting, abandoned, desecrated building (mental institution) that, in this dream, I realize was featured in a previous dream *[very early dreams, 2nd one after "my father in wheelchair . .. " -- then a re-appearance of the image 4/11/13].* But I'm suddenly concerned whether the place will still be there or if it's been totally torn down. Then I realize that it must have been, like so many of the old Kirkbride insane-asylum buildings, designated of historic architectural significance. But then I further realize (again in this dream) that the place doesn't exist except in a dream image *[though, obviously, derived from pictures of actual buildings]*.

My final thoughts as we drive along are that we don't have bathing suits which may present a problem if we want to swim when we reach the lake.

4/25/13

A very busy take-out establishment. It's set back just a bit from an old highway that seems to be in some seaside area. But no ocean in view. Whoever I'm with and I pull into the parking lot, enter the building, and place our orders at the counter. It'll be a few minutes. So I go outside and, alone now, walk up the little lane that leaves the highway close to the entry to the parking lot.

On each side I see neat, very small cottages. Otherwise the view is over a huge, Sloping field of high dune-grasses. As I walk I consider that the owners of these quaint cottages must have been really pissed when the take-out place spoiled their sense of peace and isolation. The lane seems to end at a pile of junk, part of which is the remains of a totally kicked-out and partially collapsed mobile trailer-home.

Next I seem to be on the other side of the lane from the take-out place. I'm holding a thick, dripping-juicy cheeseburger. I'm naked. I'm in a small area encircled by bushes with exceptionally long and sharp thorns. I'm very concerned how I'm going to be able to get out without getting stabbed by the thorns.

Unharmed I'm next standing next to a house on my left, which appears to be where the thorny bushes were. It's attached to a huge barn. And it seems to be my house, for when a guy emerges from a bungalow on my right I greet him and tell him that I'm moving. He says that he is too. We find that an interesting coincidence – or synchrony. As we look over to where the take-out place is very busy, he mentions something about my dismantling the barn before I move, and using the valuable siding and hand-hewn beams in décor work. I tell him that I've already done that kind of creative work.

Again (or still) I'm naked. But now I'm standing on a platform next to a railroad car, the wheels and springs and undercarriage and all quite detailed. The upper part has entry steps as if to a passenger coach, but beside them, most of the side of the car has been torn off. Inside are all kinds of equipment, some resembling commercial kitchen devices, others unrecognizable. I grab onto something and pull myself up into the car, duck this, avoid that, and manage to conceal myself behind some machine. There, perhaps I'll be able to put on underpants, I realize.

4/26/13

Second floor of a two-family house. Bunch of kid running around which I sense are Gypsy. I get a phone call concerning no local driving work today for some reason. But the trucking company wants me to take a load to Baltimore and then make a pickup in Bridgewater on the way back. I wonder if I'll have enough hours.

I'm next standing between two monstrous injection molding machines, at least 30' long and towering above. For some reason these have various turning wheels and shafts, not just hydraulics and hoses, and I'm concerned that I might get hurt.

But then it's not machines, but a cluster of professional-level speaker cabinets, various of which are facing in various directions. It may be that I'm going to be given one or more – or deafened by them.

Back to the two-family house, there's concern that with so many unraked leaves in the front yard and driveway someone could hide stolen goods. But suddenly all the leaves are gone and I'm most appreciative for whomever (probably one of the Gypsy families) raked them up.

4/27/13

Something about having trouble unlacing the wrapping of the container of a vending machine dispensed water-vapor pie.

4/29'13

Angie and I are walking along a sidewalk where the stores and view beyond seem like Kennebunk, Maine. She's suggesting that we should purchase a motorized camper and travel. I point out that with the cost of fuel added to all the other expenses of owning such a thing, it wouldn't be a wise move, much less an affordable one. Rather, I tell her, we should by a sailing yacht.

Then I'm climbing up into a narrow opening in the front wall of a store. Below, the window area is covered by a pull-down metal security barrier. I wriggle through the opening into a kitchen area. On a counter there are various bowls of fruit cocktail, but containing tomato slices. The workers want me to help myself.

Back outside, Angie and I are walking again and looking for our car, a twelve passenger van. We find it, but it's crowded full with meter maids and before we have a chance to proclaim ownership it drives away. We follow, finally finding it in a driveway leading up to a hotel overlooking the Bush summer place.

5/2/13

I'm driving alone. After passing through several small-town areas [containing images that I saw on my actual trip to Texas a couple years back] and then a huge, totally flat stretch panorama punctuated by a number of oil-drilling rigs.

I've come to a motel, settled into a room in which there's a spare door and its frame leaning against a wall next to where there'd been a smoke-pipe connection for a now-removed heating device of some kind [here, images from a door delivery to the lower-level region of a high-rise construction site during the previous day]. Soon there's a pile of various building materials in the middle of the room. I undress and drape my clothes over the pile.

In the cavernous basement area of what seems to be a very old building I'm looking for a men's room. I'm in a service (not public) area of the place, and among the several immigrants working there, one is an exceptionally beautiful woman revealing most of exquisite breasts that I admire but suddenly am accosted by a guy in a uniform who informs me that the public can no longer use the employee facilities. While making my way out of the area I'm looking for the "perfume room" for some reason.

Back at the motel which now has a long driveway through overgrown fields to reach it. At the end of the driveway I have to stop, exit the car, and climb over a sort of ridge of rock and debris to reach an alleyway that is the corridor to my room. One wall of this passage is the motel's exterior. The other is actual cliff.\

Inside again, clothes still hiding (?) the pile of stuff (that I'd scavenged?), I'm suddenly in the company of several women who are very upset. There's been a murder. The police are coming. I'm looking for the bathroom to shower. It's getting late. I can't find the shower, but I'm in a bathroom, sitting on a toilet, trying to defecate while surrounded by upset women inside, and investigating cops outside the window. I pull a tattered curtain across the window, and then find that the only material available to use as toilet paper is a roll of transparent plastic packing tape.

Jack makes a cameo appearance in a brief discussion with one of the women about concierges for kindergarteners – and that with one exception for boys only, he'd never heard of a male filling the position.

Suddenly I become aware that it must be getting very, very late and that I haven't even visited or called Angie in days while I've been on this excursion and she's been in the hospital. But I realize I've needed the time alone and maybe still do.

Then I'm with Rich, it seems, and we're considering the massive resort renovation job we're about to begin. At the foot of a hill is the parking lot from which we first have to remove the top layer of paving – which is the oriental rug in my living room. Rich starts pulling it up in strips. But then we're up at a higher level of the grounds. On one side there's a hedge of shrubs, each growing out of closely-spaced bores in a granite wall. We consider how hard it's going to be to remove the myriad from the granite, some of which now is seen to be carved like cornice molding. I reach to touch a piece and it falls with a splash into the pool, now seen just beyond and below.

Finally, Angie and I are walking along a raised part of a side-by-side two-level sidewalk along a busy street. People of all ages and ethnicities and dress are walking, running, skate-boarding, scootering in either direction. Some are standing or sitting alone, or in groups which are little clusters of conversations in various languages. We walk along somewhat downhill and I realize that even here, I'm heading to the massive resort-rehabilitation job I've been contracted to do and that the oriental carpet parking lot surface has intriguingly reappeared untorn at that lower region we approach as we walk down the sloping drive.

5/3/13

With Ron, the dispatcher at work and we're trying to find the location of where I'm to make a delivery. Ron doesn't have a smart phone and doesn't know how to research online.

Driving along back roads through very rural farming region with Angie and we see a decrepit, miniature barn with arched windows and both realize it will make a nice house. In somehow towing it behind us I've become rather covered with manure and dirt -- and Angie, and now an unseen woman passenger with us, comment on my body odor.

At the head of the driveway of the house in Franklin we're meeting with a representative from some bank regarding mortgage financing that may be held up due to some court decision concerning an accident. I realize I no longer have cash-on-hand to cover what I'd previously have been able to finance without a mortgage.

Still seemingly at the top of the driveway I'm atop a veritable Rube-Goldberg wood framework that's like a superstructure atop a truck chassis which appears to be powered by horses or oxen, though neither are evident. I'm nailing a piece of 2x4 with a spike which bends, forcing me to climb down to acquire another. Back atop I hear some guy talking about living in the thing like a derelict . . .but then it's Marie [previous next door neighbor and Angie's best friend] consoling and advising Angie about cancer treatment.

As Angie and I ride along a road beside an interstate (Mass Pike?), some other woman is driving. We look at the traffic heading Eastward toward Boston and I comment that since the end of a holiday weekend, it's a good thing we're on a back road and not the highway which will soon be almost unmoving traffic jam all the way back to route 495. (It doesn't seem to function in the logic and reasoning of this part of the dream that we're heading Westward!!)

5/6/13

In an upstairs room an orgy seems to be in progress. Naked young men and women are standing, dancing, cavorting on the numerous tables. Suddenly someone comes in and the party breaks up. I descend stairs from the orgy site and come to a lobby of a medical facility where numerous medical people are as confused as I about who I should be about to consult with.

On the way to the exit from the lobby I encounter a woman kind of helping along and almost holding up an elderly man who I recognize as the composer Edward Grieg. He's wearing an overcoat so long that it almost touches the ground, but still he looks cold, frail. My intention had been to rob these two people as the emerged from behind the curtain of a voting booth. But seeing how decrepit Grieg looks, I change my mind.

Suddenly, from the same lobby, I'm carrying folding metal chairs out the door and over a patch of parking lot, a strip of grass. From there I slid them about four feet down a slanted wall, making sort of leaning stacks against the wall – making sure that only one type of folding chair is in a stack. A guy down below is tallying the chairs and then loading them into a vehicle.

5/14/13

I've parked my tractor-trailer rig in the middle of a lot that seems to be surrounded by residences (houses). And, naked, I'm in someone's house, engaged in some conversation and hospitality. But soon I realize that I've lingered too long, for I still have a rather full trailer-load of freight to be delivered to an auto parts place in Franklin, MA.

To exit the building I've been in I have to cross what appears more like a loading dock than a back porch or patio. But I easily descend to the tar parking area, looking for my truck which isn't where I left it. Someone has moved it (probably because it was blocking other vehicles). Now it's way, way over at the extreme end of the lot. At about the first step towards it I'm suddenly immersed up to my chest in a deep puddle.

A vague continuation of the dream has me trying to find a place to turn the rig around so that I can proceed in the opposite direction on the road I'm on.

> For some reason, (but then again, maybe for no reason), for this the interim between the above and the below dreams, the frequency of dreaming itself decreased significantly. Some nights I didn't seem to dream at all. And the dreams that I did vaguely experience, were no only vague, but fleeting from wakened consciousness. Thus I couldn't "remember", "recall", and write them up.

5/19/13

Grid streets as un Back Bay Boston. But the wood-frame two and three-family buildings on embankments on each side of the streets had two or three floors of porches on their facades. So the structures made it seem more like I was in Somerville or Medford.

I didn't feel lost, but I couldn't find my way to some destination. I went around a block a couple times, over to another and followed its one-way street all the way to the end. There, the surroundings appeared to be sparse houses and cottages built on seaside marshland.

Back I was in the grid streets. I was driving what had been my aunt Marj's 1988 Oldsmobile and, to my horror, I suddenly noticed that its hood was missing. Had I lost it back at the marshland region, I wondered.

But I'd parked in a lot behind buildings on a Main Street: first floor stores with offices or housing above. Adjacent to the lot I seem to have bought a three story, white colored, apartment house and I was going to live in one of the apartments. But having climbed the stairs to the second floor I was unable to enter the unit. So up to the third, but I had no key.

On the first floor of this building I did get into the apartment. In the bathroom I found my nephew-in-law, Rob, having problems with some plumbing work.. He was outside, trying to feed something through an access panel in the back wall. I reached to help him, but it was a sheet of paper he was dealing with, and with my involvement it crumpled.

So he and I went upstairs in what had become another building, this one beside a field in which cars were lined up waiting to get a parking space. The top-floor food emporium was very busy. Rob and I moved through the mass of people to place our orders. But I had to make a phone call to my dispatcher regarding not having been able to find what I was looking for in the grid-street area. Rob appeared carrying our orders just as I was told that I had to immediately make a pickup at the Milton McDonalds. Considering the time of day, traffic, and not knowing where I was, I conveyed that I didn't think that would be possible.

Rob and I seemed to take the food with us. In front of the place. Rowdy teenage boys, a couple with bloated, bare bellies, were hanging and tussling around in front of the first floor karate or video-game establishment.

As were leaving in the hoodless car, I watched a tiny Asian woman trying to exit the parking lot. Nobody in the endless stream of cars waiting to park would let her through the line.

5/21

Throwing things over a fence. Where, what, why unknown. But in the gutter on the other side of the fence I'm with others picking up objects and scooping up what seem to be mounds and spires of semi-solid (perhaps gelatinous) white stuff and putting it in a car.

I'm in the mansion of someone or other who seems to be having a party with my in-laws (of a much younger age than now) on the first floor. From the second level balcony I look out over a garage where a boat is stored.

A woman, very much in a hurry, comes up the metal stairs from the garage, looks down the corridor, around a corner, sees me. And before she says a word I ask/say to her "Bathroom!?" She looks desperately relieved as I point to the door of the loo.

5/22/13

Beside the street, beyond a tipped and torn and otherwise desecrated chain link fence, there seems to be a vast area that might be the remnants (or ruination) of some military base. Or maybe a shipbuilding facility (in that there's a vague resemblance to the Fore River Ship Yard in Quincy, MA.

After some distance of this I find myself in a rambling area inside a room. A kind of corridor has been established between the outside walls and plywood panels, continuous around the "inner" part of the passageway. On the panels are hundreds of posters that have been hand lettered. Apparently every kindergarten-through grade school kid in the state has been lettering the posters. From top to bottom of the 8' high panels the posters are rather carelessly positioned, some tipped, irregularly spaced, etc. The text scrawled upon them has something to do with the facility that I'd seen beyond the chain link fence.

After almost completely circling the room, scanning the posters as I go, I find myself within an area (within the plywood panels?). There, someone whose dress and demeanor suggest a salesman is sort of presenting an adolescent girl to another man. This other, in tux, with monocle, holding cane, tall, I assume to be Daddy Warbucks. Within whatever business context is going on, at first the child is of no interest to him. The scenario then subtly seems theatric, even on-stage. And next the salesman is actually singing something, "Undressed below the knees, you'll find her most alluring" and I marvel (still dreaming) at the "play-on-morality-concept" of those lyrics. An actual old Broadway show states, "In olden times a glimpse of stocking was looked on as something shocking." And also I sense that there's a subliminal perversion in this allusion to Little Orphan Annie.

Awake, it occurs to me that I've dreamt a critique of the perversity of propositions involving private capital and the military-industrial complex.

6/11/13

I'm naked. In large back room of factory or warehouse. Smoking cigarette down to butt, but there are two, and I throw the longer one on the floor and grind it out, only then realizing it should have been the short one, for I could have had a few more drags on the longer one.

A special-delivery comes, documents in a see-through envelope. The delivery guy and someone concerned with receiving the material converse for a moment, the only words clear being that the delivery charge is $785.00. I consider that I should get into that kind of delivery business rather than trucking. The Jamaican dock worker *[from my trucking job]* wants something taken off the bulletin board so that he can redeem it for cash.

A brief interlude of vague ideas and images about meeting another truck driver from Maine so we could swap rigs, then something about taking something to New Jersey.

But the realm now seems to be a kitchen facility of a closed-up school or other institution. The vast walk-in freezer has been opened after years. Huge boxes containing food are being taken out, and I'm shown in one of them. Still frozen solid are hundreds of pounds of cold cuts, most obvious being salami in this case. Some looks fresh, but other parts are obviously seriously freezer-burned (the refrigeration had not been shut-off).

A porch roof, perhaps 20' wide, and a greater dimension stretching out over a roadway. Just on the other side of the road is the ocean. The roof has no outer supports (columns), but is cantilevered from whatever building protrudes from. Seems that as part of the seaside amusement area, paying patrons could manipulate something or other to make one extension or other of the roof rise or lower. But then it was realized that this was going to result in the whole thing coming loose.

I've wound around roads in a hilly region which has turned into a portly body of some well-known entertainer around which I (now microbe-size) make my way. I come to several other naked young men. They're in a sort of sluice through which water races, and they're teasing each other, especially a heavy-set guy with prolific chest hair (known, but unseen in the dream, to be red). They're comparing his hair to cinnamon and him to a pastry.

Back outside in the hilly area I realize that the bridge I've crossed has totally collapsed. As I walk along beside an old highway I consider that I may be blamed for something, but that I've done nothing wrong at all. It was spontaneous destruction.

I drive uphill away from a house that faces the sea out on a kind of peninsula. Something concerning medicine or psychotherapy goes on there and has involved me. But I'm leaving until I somehow get a message that I have to go back if I can. At high speed in reverse, I turn onto the road to the place. The steering wheel whips around as I release it and the car straightens out of the turn.

Standing on a long loading dock, I'm ready to leave the premises. But as I look down, I realize that the ground level is flooded with at least 4' of water, and that Angie and the car she's in, are all but submerged. I watch the exhaust bubble into the water and up to sort of erupt like pimples at the surface and I think of farting in a bathtub.

6/11/13

A vast cellar, at least 100' long. It's divided into two parts, one a few steps higher than the other. The width of both combined is more than 100'. The ceiling is low. Here and there are typical house cellar windows. The floor is strewn with debris and piled with dirt and silt.

I'm instructing young people (college-age) that to clean the place it's not necessary to carry everything over to the one egress. Rather, throw things out the several windows.

I return some time later to find the lower half of the place totally bare, pristine clean, still wet here and there from washing. The upper part is already partly furnished with restaurant booths, and in preparation for an opening there are a few people gathered. Some food (cold cuts, pastries) is available. I take a coffee role and proceed to consult regarding remaining work to be done before the official opening. One of the items is a 10' diameter combination smoke and exhaust pipe that will cross part of the roof. I'm on the roof measuring.

But suddenly I'm in a barber shop and counting out nickels, dimes, and a few quarters into a depression made in the cloth draped over me. The haircut cost $12.50.

Next I'm moving (by hand) a truck trailer, pushing it somewhat behind another into a dock space. That done, I'm approaching the entrance to the building with someone else, who suddenly jumps on me and is biting my shoulder. But then I'm going upstairs and finding a little restaurant in what had been an apartment. I know the proprietor, but had not known of his enterprise. We exchange niceties and I say I'll have to try his cuisine another time.

Back at the cellar restaurant. I'm double checking measurements, then in a hallway to an exit. A young woman and I have conversed about something, seemed attracted to one another, and mutually approached to kiss. But I misinterpret, and rather than just "peck" lips, I embrace her and start to truly kiss her. She reacts with trauma and rage and races out of the place. I follow, trying to apologize and explain my error of assumption.

Outside, I'm looking down as if from the top of The Blue Hills. I'm only dressed in shirt and pants. No coat. It's the middle of the night. I'll have to walk down the mountain to get back to Boston. But as I look into the distance below, the strand of illumination I see suggests that I'm looking at Route 93 or even route 24 going Southward, thus the opposite direction from Boston.

On the roof of the cellar restaurant, I've completed the installation of the piping for the exhaust of the smoke from the broilers and wood grille. I listen, satisfied that there are no leaks to result in noise pollution and possible complaints.

10/13/13

Coming out of the doorway of a three-decker. A dog on a leash. Huge snowbank beside the porch landing, and dog jumps down between it and structure. I follow dog out to street where it suddenly dives into the snow and disappears. It's all I can do to pull him out, offer some food which he scoffs before diving in again. I realize I can extract him if I exert ultimate effort (and the leash doesn't break).

In a building with vague suggestions of the Bear Hill Golf Club (where aunt Marj used to go and occasionally take us to dinner). To get to the part where I'm to dine I have to grab onto an overhead pipe and swing my legs up onto the upper level of a corridor which seems to be severed at that point into two sections. The height difference is a good five feet or more and I have difficulty swinging my body over to the upper level.

Dining in a rear upstairs room, no details. Look for rest room, at first entering ladies room where there's a dog (different one) that runs out. I find the men's room.

Next, Angie and I are amid a crowd of people in an almost dark downstairs area. The chamber seems tenement-like, but our purpose there is for me to sign the bill for the dinner we've had. At the table is David Latham. I inform him that I'll be sending a check. He's risen from the table and we go to the front of the place where he's telling me on no uncertain terms that I owe nothing.

At that point I'm getting very concerned about having enough time to get to the airport to fly to Texas for visit with Greg. I can't seem to find my copy of the departure schedule.

Angie and I exit the place going down many steps to the street-level. There, she forges ahead of me, on the opposite side of the street. The area seems like a fusion of Dorchester and Malden's Linden section. I'm very concerned about getting to the airport. We're walking!!!

Suddenly I'm crouched beside what seems to be a somewhat gaping hole in a commercial building. [Image from a movie scene of wartime destruction]. In the debris of the basement there's an operating donut shop. I didn't have enough cash regarding the bill for our meal, but now only have hills large enough that I don't want to break just for donuts. So I take out my change purse and am counting quarters, then times and nickels, finally enough for the cost.

Then back on the street. I catch up with Angie, who's quietly raging at me about not paying attention to her, trying to be the Mr. know-it-all big-shot, and I'm realizing the obvious characteristics that had been diagnosed as schizophrenic years ago. As I try to communicate with her I realize that some people who are walking along near us can hear me.

Then Angie and I are in the middle the McGrath Highway (Somerville) as we continue walking toward the airport. I'm trying to get her to calm down, to explain her thinking rather than excress (explode) her emotions. "That's something Madelaine would have done!!!" she says. (Madelaine, her sister who'd died a few years prior).

It finally comes out that Angie thought my interchange with Latham about the bill was to weasel (or connive or lie) my way out of paying it. "So maybe I'm stupid.", Angie's anger starts to transmute to hurt.

I begin by going with the "stupid" and examples from this outburst, such as her "going off" in reaction without first going into the issue to ascertain just what it represented – just because it seemed like . . . didn't mean it was!! Just because Madelaine would have . . . didn't mean that I was re-enacting Madelaine's manipulations.

And I quickly transformed the whole context as I tell Angie that she should realize she isn't stupid at all!! She was exceptionally creative and discerning, recognizing patterns and similarities in people and in situations. "That's creativity, not stupidity. You're able to combine aspects of experience into present episodes (like scenes, chapters) in which you re-create a "stage" of your life in which you had to just hide/suppress your feelings. Now you're able to release them, express them, perform them. That's artistic ability, Creativity. Nothing stupid about that except not recognizing it."

We walk along closely, silently for a minute. Then I explain to her that the bill for our dinner was processed before a gratuity was added. I didn't have enough cash on me to cover it. Thus I was telling Latham that I would send a check to reimburse him for what he'd temporarily pay for the tip.

There's a sudden glimpse of a ultra-high-end sailing yacht, either beside the highway we walk, or it might have been passing us on a trailer. The sides of the stern hull flare out as glass "bubbles", providing floor-to overhead view in and out of the magnificent craft.

[On waking, I'm instantly curious what the snow-burrowing dog represents, if anything other than a composite totally unrelated images from several movies I'd watched within the last few days. But regarding the dinner and Angie and flying to visit Greg segment . . . . the consideration came to me that this was a sort of "summation" of past situations. And the anxiety about getting to the airport for the trip, an actually scheduled visit with Greg and family]?

[In addition to "summation" the turmoil and trauma of the past involving Angie and family and Angie and Greg and Angie and M . . . was this dream a premonition? Was I glimpsing the possibility that I (with Angie at peace and only with me "in spirit") might not make it to the airport? I might take to the sky, figuratively (and inversely *in locus*), first?]

[I went back to sleep after entering the above and dreamed . . .]

I'm standing at the kind of counter you'd see in an ice cream shop. Next to me is a young woman at a cash register. I've mentioned to her something about not knowing how much the gratuity should be *[this dream involving the dinner bill etc. from the previous dream!!]* She tells me she can easily just access the transaction record. I tell her that she can't, because the dinner took place at another establishment.

On the other side of the counter there's a group of college-age people. I'm now with them and one, a very small girl, has mentioned something about hair styling being designated by Daniel.

I ask if she's referring to the Book of Daniel in the Bible.

She says, yes, and I notice now that she is not a whole person, rather just a glazed clay (or porcelain) head on a stand. And her head is bald as she seems to be defending something in discussion with the group [not seen but known to be there] around her.

Suddenly her head is adorned with dreadlocks, extremely tightly "woven" or "braided". Secured within the end, and pointing down from each strand of hair, are finely hewn shards of ivory or bone, their extremes almost as sharp as hypodermic needles. [images from an anthropology documentary I'd watched the night before – the dreadlocks just extensions of "nappy hair" of aboriginals, and the sharp points transferred from arrow- and spear-point utility to adornment].

And suddenly I was awake (though even after 12 hours), not really motivated to get up!!

12/27/13

Looking up a drive into a short drive that I realize (though don't recognize) leads to the courtyard of the little estate that my uncle Bill used to occupy. But now the paved area (below much-exaggerated cliffs atop which the house sits) is filled with debris consisting of great piece of concrete beams with reinforcing rods sticking out both ends, steel highway berm materials all bent and wrecked, and other unidentifiable wreck and ruin.

Concerned, I and some companion start up the drive. But it has become steep hillside. Toward the crest an immense wolf lies on his side and howls, but pays us no heed as we continue over the crest.

Down below there's an area somewhat reminiscent of "uncle Bill's" locale, but as we suddenly find ourselves down on that level, it has become an entrance hall of a massive, decrepit, stinking and strewn tenement building. At the top of a couple flights of stairs we come to a dead-end landing. High on one wall there's a narrow window, and when we've found chairs to stand on we're able to see down into an apartment where cousins-in-law Terri and Helen are talking on their cell phones, thus not noticing even our rapping on the window.

As well as the window glass (which we break), there are woven rods across the window opening. We start to bend and break these when my son Jack (who's suddenly appeared as my companion) considers that this might get us in trouble for vandalism or destruction of property.

And then, with no segue, I'm driving a barely running vehicle along Memorial Drive in Cambridge until it suddenly has narrowed to a steeply descending drive-way down into a junk-filled region behind totally derelict buildings. This is an auto repair realm and I get to a big, rusted roll-up door bang my fists on it. It opens. An interior mesh door opens. The British sports car (a Triumph or MG of '40s vintage) sputts and smokes its way into the building with hardly an inch to spare between all sorts of vehicles piled on each other.

Now I'm almost in a panic about having something to drive so that I can get to work, and first, get Angie (who has now replaced Jack as my passenger) home. I inquire whether I can rent something operable for a couple days. The employee who has let me in (at the last second before they'd have been closed), tells me he'll have to consult with the management person (with whom I've usually conducted any business).

While he's gone, I consider a worst-case scenario. I'll just have purchase a decent car for whatever it costs, minus whatever I'll be allowed for the trade-in of my "antique" wreck.

He comes back and relates the suggestion/solution.

Since hardly any of the other cars I've left there have sold, rather than leave another, I can swap the present one for a previous for a couple days and then choose which I'll prefer to keep (and which leave with them) until the next such transaction.

[The sudden cessation (at least it seems so) of this dream awakens me 2 hours prior to my usual time. Rather than relieve and re-sleep, I overcome take care of the former and overcome the urge for the latter . . . . and type this up on computer.]

12/31, 2013

Son Jack has decided to change his investment operations to include more free-lance opportunities and income. Thus his position at Merrill Lynch will be available. He somewhat jokingly asks if I'd be interested in taking his place.

When I express interest he takes me to an upper floor in the building. The view out over San Diego is impressive, but more so is the actual office space he has been utilizing. It occupies a sort balcony (comparable to a drawer that can be opened out from, or closed back into, the building). On it are 6 cubicles that actually have a closer resemblance to booths in a restaurant.

The whole balcony-space rents for $2500 per month, but when he mentions that I'd be able to rent just one or two of the 6 spaces, I'm interested. For one space, that little-over $400 would put me in a position of preferential access to market trends, and also in the company of investment professionals.

But without any transition in the dream, I'm next in the basement area of the building, next to what might be a huge elevator-shaft sub-structure. Think a two-story high steel-bar-walled cage perhaps 30' x 30' – but ascending above it not an elevator shaft. Rather, a masonry chimney that must reach above the roof of the building.

The chimney is to be imploded within the building. And this is to happen with me and whomever else (unseen others) right there next to the "cage" sub-structure in the vast basement.

Detonations are heard. From puffing silt and soot to various sized unto massive concrete and brick and stone shards plunge down within the cage, filling it up, distorting it outward to an extent that I feared it would rupture and we'd be buried in the debris. But suddenly it's all over and the rubble has been safely contained.

Outside the building, I'm apparently looking for a way to get back in. At one point there seems to be a passageway through shrubs, but then I come to where one of a pair of columns crooked, thus blocking my way on in.

I realize it must have been displaced by the implosion of the chimney.

[I pray that this dream has no premonitory/symbolic significance concerning market (DOW etc.) valuation-futures!!]

Part II

Recognizably just south of Lexington Center, MA on Mass. Avenue. I'm driving my tractor-trailer rig toward Boston. I'm dressed in hooded pajamas. I'm exhausted and relieved to see a sign in the yard of a large house. It states that there are rooms available for tired truckers.

I park the truck, walk cross the Ave, ascend the sloped yard, my baggy pajamas almost tripping me.

On the back porch I'm talking with a middle-aged, somewhat portly, but attractive woman who's telling me her very French name – but that her lineage is Jewish, though she doesn't know the details of how her forebears got from where to where and ended up in Canada before moving down to the States.

Inside, she's made me something to eat and seems intent on starting some kind of relationship which would have me visiting her at least weekly. She announces that her mother is about to enter the room, and that she's a very formal, classical lady. A regal, almost miniature, elderly woman comes into the room. I rise, approach her as I somewhat bow, and express "honor" to meet her (considering that kissing her hand might be a bit excessive, or even an affront from a truck driver in pajamas).

On the floor beneath the table to which I've returned to my meal, there's a baby boy. My hostess begins telling about the problems with caring for the child (now somewhat implying that my relationship might be with the child as well as with the woman.

An attractive woman in her twenties is introduced to me as my hostess's sister, and the concerns about the baby amid the tomato slices and green pepper pieces and onion arcs on the floor now includes sister. That the baby is the fault in relationships is being presented by both women – and it's an effort for me not to just blurt out that it's not the kid; it's that they aren't competent to care for the kid. And I picture myself getting down on the floor, cleaning up the mess, and playing with the obviously neglected baby.

But suddenly I'm having to explain that I can't stay long. I'm due in Weymouth for Xmas dinner with Diana (my ex-wife) and her family. But I make tentative arrangements to stop at least once a week and visit my new French-Jewish friends (not a French-Jewish girlfriend, though, I tactfully stress). When I look into the dining room to say goodbye to sister, I see that she has set up a bunch of action figures and dolls on the far side of the table. On her end, she's singing and speaking into a karaoke device.

I exit the house and am now in a fenced-in yard, the fence itself patched and pieced, the yard overgrown and strewn with stuff. Suddenly there's a big, shaggy sheep, then another. And then a couple border collie dogs appear and go about a almost artistic duet of herding the sheep.

But short of accomplishing any containment, one of the sheep manages to squeeze through an opening between rotted fence boards. A dog follows. And I, next, outside the fence but through a gate.

Part III
And next I'm driving on the McGrath Highway in Cambridge, heading toward Boston. Where all kinds of buildings should be on the right, there's but a huge freight yard. And closest to the highway, almost too close for my comfort, there's a tractor-trailer rig with rail-car wheels attached. It on the rails and I on the road race along side-by-side.

Part IV
And then in a car but next on a bike but in a car again and I can't find the way from route 109 in Millis to the court building in Wrentham. I seem to be wandering through rain-drenched European villages and between hedgerows and through barnyards and finally find someone from whom to ask directions.

A block away is the Court building. I enter through a rear door My being there has something to do with registration of a motor vehicle, but other than some court personnel being exceptionally friendly, no further information or imagery transpired.

[some segments of the above derived from my reading through Exodus on 12/30 – Jews, sheep. The train and trucking images are just ongoing brain residue from my years in the freight-delivery business and the areas and scenes of my activities. Regarding Merrill Lynch and Jack, he and I spoke on the phone that evening, though no mention of a career change was made. The chimney implosion? Actual from website ("Controlled Demolition, Inc.") – from a satiric piece in "The Onion" exhorting homeowners to have factory chimneys built so that they, as private citizens, can contribute to the patriotic display of toxic fumes and acid rain along with

corporate echelons . . . . or maybe an actual Freudian dream- revelation of revelation of ended revelation?]

1/2/14/13

Part I

On a trip in what had been my Aunt Marj's 1984 Oldsmobile. With me are Jack, Vincent, and several others. The car, big as it is, is full of people inbetween whom are stuffed all kinds of things: blankets, trash bags, duffels, and more.

Heading up a steep hill on a two-lane highway we pass a couple dangerous-looking men who walk toward the car as if threatening. But we surmount the crest of the hill and start down and they're gone. In front of us the land drops into a gorge, likely where there's a river. The road crosses a bridge with tall pilasters to which the supporting cables are attached as in a typical suspension bridge. But atop the pilasters there seems to be geologic formation – the effect being that the bridge has been built by tunneling through a mountain!

Beyond that, we come to an intersection with a larger highway. Signs indicate that Boston is to the right, but we want to head in the opposite direction. The opposite direction is North . . . and Boston, we know for sure, is North of where we are. We turn onto the highway and in no time come to an intersection, the several confluent streets joining at the center of some city or other, stores and gas stations and other commercial enterprise all around us.

Double-parking, some from the car go into a variety store/gas station to ask directions. They come back out bearing snacks and we're on our way and in no time I find that the car and I are parked in the front yard of a somewhat rural house. On the steps a couple of the passengers sit, and somehow those couple others in the car with me and I realize that all involved in the present locale are our family members. But we have to be on our way. I've backed out onto the street and on down a side street, reversed and next I'm driving slowly by the house. Only Jack seems to missing from the passengers and someone in the car mentions that he's probably lingering in the house (Chris's father-in-law's?) in order to sell an income indemnification policy. There's a small pond off to the side as we drive on away from there. Stretched partway into the pond, but part on the land, is some kind of creature that looks like a skatefish or stingray. I'm concerned whether Jack's in the car or not.

Part II

A vast, almost empty, industrial interior that seems to have once been a commercial kitchen. Little remains but some stainless steel tables. Near one on which I lean, a young woman is explaining to others that she's getting married because she's found out that she's pregnant. There are some negative reactions from those unseen (but sensed to be female co-workers): whether she loves the father should be considered, they say; whether she's in a position to support and raise a child too.

The young woman replies that in contexts as profound and complex as the replication of life itself, the actuality (pregnancy/birth) should be the primacy and determination beyond other factors. Pregnancy IS! Emotional relationships , compat-abilities, and such are variables of which the evaluations should be integers implicit in the functional formulae of living lifespans (not just lubricious/superficial youth spans) and providing ongoing lives (children) with functional formats of existence. And, she continues, the means or ability to raise children is not to be a proportionate extrapolation from some 1st-World Western Civilization Gross Domestic Product-determined ethos. Within and from the most "impoverished" realms of the earth are the ways and means for actual human-being fulfillment provided by nature's aspects inclusive of beauty, man's nature incarnate in recognizing not only the beauty but the essence (even as survival) of nature, and beyond that in evolutionary and even more creationistic-paradigm processes of . . . . yes . . . . human advance.

From the primal-stream of migration-motivation . . . . . to the present spectacular spectra of technological and aesthetic-creativities, the innate potential of mankind made should far out-value the intimate personal perspective of love-making.

Part III

It seems that in exiting the above realm I've come to an alley sloping down steeply between various and sundry wrecked or abandoned cars and trucks, some piled atop others. But seen behind these there's somewhat open land where adolescents are grouped. A bit on down some of the kids have come between the junks and I realize that they all seem to have some sort of disability or distortion. One I notice has almost elephantiasis-enlargement of a leg and an arm. Another is just obese all over. And closest to me on young boy reveals that one his legs ends not with a foot, but a sharp shard of bones.

Seeing that I'm staring he laughs, pulling up the pant-leg a bit more. "That's the point!" he says.

On down and I'm inside a room totally crowded with mostly teenage girls. I realize this must be the "living room" of a group home for the disabled and disadvantaged. But when I manage to squeeze myself between supple bodies and near a window for some air as antidote for the overwhelming perfume and pheromone intoxication (nothing actually smelled in the dream – I've never experienced an olfactory-actual dream . . . has anyone???) . . . I reach the window and I'm outside!!

Over a short walk I come to a staircase up to a porch. On the porch is a beautiful young girl who is explaining something or other and showing me various and sundry (none detailed visually in the dream). I sense that all this "introduction and orientation"? is for a purpose and the next thing I know she's plastered herself frontally against me and is breathing heavily and I'm responding physically but retorting cognitively, "I should have known this would happen".

Part IV

I still seem to be in the realm of the above – only now the junks and kids are above the level where there are a couple stores, streets, and the vehicles are just parked, not piled. Beside me is a truck with some mural painted on its side. Howie Strathie (my old frat. buddy and lifetime friend) has just asked me if I've prepared my poop to prosper. I answer his typical scatological-laced humorous expression. "No, I've conservatively secured it in a CD, which in this case stands for Ceramic Depository.

We stroll a bit along the sidewalk and notice (in the dream) that I'm noticing that in the dream (earlier part) the creature part-in the pond now is a creature partway in the pond beside where Howie and I stroll. It looks to be about twenty feet long, perhaps almost as much wide. Not a stingray. "A skate? Inland this far?" I ask.

"It's a mammoth turtle", Howie informs me. On its back.

And now I see. The head and front half of the creature is submerged in the pond. The rest of it is sprawled, upon its back, on the land beside the water. Others are now gathered and it seems we all assume the thing is dead. But then there's noticeable vibration of the water. And next, discernable now to be turtle feet, all four begin kind of coordinated motions. And this soon has enabled the creature to begin shifting its whole body back and forth at least a foot, then more, then even more and all the while kind of arcing the reciprocations so that the front-quarters are turning toward the land and using the back (downward-side) of the feet almost like flippers, soon it has turned almost toward the land . . and all the way and at the same time with a sudden flip it's right-side-up . . . and with an astounding thrust of its hind legs it rockets out from the water and plot of land and spectators and up and over the truck with the mural and . . . *[at that point the damned phone rang in actuality].*

2014

1/8/14

I'm explaining to unseen others with me that I'm going to move from my house. We're looking out over my backyard – which is a vast expanse of wasteland including gravel and sand pits and junkyards and areas of collapsing warehouses and dirt-bike trails embroidering other vistas of desolation and desecration.

Next, perhaps on the way to where my new residence will be (by going North on rte. 495 in part), I'm driving a tractor-trailer rig and turn East on the first exit road, then off it up a driveway into an industrial area. I park and go into an office building to inquire where I should deliver my freight. Attractive young women are playing pool in offices.

The alley which I look down on from a second-floor level is in Boston. On one side of it there's a rather famous restaurant, and the passageway comes to a dead-end. The ground level is piled with debris to which I and others are contributing pieces of a wooden staircase. But suddenly on the ground, we're attempting to move pieces and other stuff back to the upper level.

But this Boston scenario has now become the part of the Franklin, MA house from which I'm moving. Suddenly one of the truck drivers appears from my prior job (I'd retired, but 2 years after moving – not before!) He's holding a half-full bottle of Gatorade, and explaining that I'd left it behind at work and that I should have it. I'm most appreciative of his having made the 100 mile round trip for me, and I provide him with some of the staircase parts and other debris from the alley, apparently now part of my property, to take back for his own property.

1/23/14

    The locale appears to be a sound stage where a family sit-com is being filmed. But it also seems to be the playroom of my actual residence. Unseen therein is my family. My wife has insisted that she has to go to work, that earning income is a priority, and that's her role. To her and the kids (none of them seen in the dream) I state that it's come to a society role-reversal when the husband bitches to the wife that she her career is more important than her marriage and motherhood. I'm being a bit facetious, putting her on, but making a point. Nonetheless, she departs (unseen) for her job, leaving me with the kids.

    To whom I'm explaining how I built antique house frames with hand hewn, tongue and groove, beams. There were roofs on these structures, but no outside walls. As I talk, I'm on the second floor of one, another frame a bit away on a hillside.

    Suddenly I'm in a desolate lot with a massive warehouse building to one side rising several stories of blank, brick wall. At ground level a rather cavernous opening seems to penetrate into, probably, a loading dock. But I'm in a vehicle on the lot outside, listening to children's voices from around the corner of the building. I hope-they won't come closer, for I'm now looking into the opened roll-up door of a box truck in front of me. There's an access step halfway between the ground and the empty interior of the truck. For some reason it's ominous, but I realize I may be too exhausted to leave, and I'm unable to call home.

The next area resembles the outermost reaches, beyond the runways, of some airport. But I realize that the chain link fence extending to infinity in both directions beside me, separates this wasteland from the immense parking area surrounding a superbowl-dimension sports stadium. The video of a baby's astounding singing has gone viral, and the infant, I somehow know, is going to perform at the opening of the event. And I'm there, now playing a piano as accompaniment to the tiny voice I hear performing "God Bless America". I realize that, ,massively amplified through the sound system, the result must be acoustically and musically all but operatic and astounding.

1/24/14

In a shopping mall, upper floor, stores to each side. In front of me young women with their pants cut away to reveal their buttock. They're tattooing each other with pens. But next it's just one woman in a station wagon, the tailgate open. And her anus is being spot-welded and she's screaming.

A kind of catwalk or scaffolding several stories up and circling a whole building. With me is the owner of some construction materials company. He's concerned with work on the place, but he can't remember his name,. Suddenly we're inside where various corridors and rooms are almost chaotic collages of embellished décor. With one of my sons, I start removing these veneers (embossed, paper mache. Plaster castings, wood carvings, steel etc. The final glimpse of this realm is brightened when daylight streams into the corridor through long-covered arched windows.

Driving around blocks in downtown Boston. Here, a truck backed into the midst of a crowded parking lot to make a delivery. There, a short bridge with construction materials stacked out into the right-of-way. I hit a pile of little wood blocks.

A suburban/rural area. On foot I circle a building's surrounding field, near it, and at first am inside the first floor where there's either a pharmacy or variety store. But suddenly I'm again climbing the stairs to enter the place. I'm craving gum drops which I've bought there before. But I see a "closed" sign on the door.

In a VW bug. I have a bunch of documents to delivery for air transport. First I pass an empty lot that I realize had been the site of my town's parochial school. I'd not previously noticed the building had been torn down. On I drive, coming into an arena-like area. An elevated office (like a little trailer set up on beams) is my destination for delivery. A metal stairway rises to the door and I drive right up and park on the landing. Unseen, several people associated with the place are good-naturedly hassling me about delivering air freight to them, who'll have to deliver it to the airport – when it should have been delivered directly to the air carrier. They have no gum drops. I'm back in the VW bug, ascertain that there are stairs going down in front of me, and start the engine.

1/26/14

An upper room somewhere. It's come to pass that I've entered this chamber through the door behind me. Beside me there's a sofa against the wall. But behold, there comes unto being a space between the back of the sofa and the wall. And at floor level, from beneath the sofa, I see wisps or fumes emanating. And these become the image of a transparent Tammy Faye (disgraced wife of the disgraced televangelist some years back).

Her apparition rises to stand beside me and interrogate me. "Do you personally know God?"

I embark upon a profound statement, assuring her that I do know god very well, for God is the (combined) systemic and substantive universality of existence that formed and forms the universe and includes the miraculous "existential harmonic" of awareness – especially that of man, which has the potential (wired-in domain) of "knowing" of the whole universal expanse (Big Bang, sub-particulate-unto social evolution, even one's own genetic dimension).

I've hardly begun this explanation of my "religious" belief in contrast of hers. But suddenly there is facing me a guy. In the dream I recognize him as a combination of my ex-daughter-in-law's late father – and my late wife's brother-in-law.

He interrogates me, "But what does the Bible say?"

I retort, "You're the evangelical one. What does It say?"

"I don't know," he replies.

I tell him, "I do, for I've recently read the whole New Testaments and am over half way through the Old, studying the writings and their meanings and lack thereof.

[This latter is actuality – part of my research already published as *CREATIONIST LITERALISM, A GENESISIAN HERESY* . . and absolute impossibility, and *GOD IS NOT AN OLD, BEARDED WHITE GUY IN THE SKY.*]

But I'm next driving along a street. I pull into the parking area surrounding the construction of a building. Somehow Only the exterior cement block walls and roof trusses are erected so far. Somehow I'm informed it's to be a new Grossman's building materials outlet and I consider that not too far away are 2 Home Depots and a Lowes.

I'm next laying some kind of heavy fabric across the roof trusses, from front to back of the structure. The materials resembles that of the sleeping bag I'm actually in – but has structural properties such that I can walk on it. Yet it cuts easily (front to back) with a razor blade I have. Where there's an excessive overlap, I slice and extract a thin excess and toss it over the side [in the previous day's reading had been information about a Frank Lloyd Wright house sheathed in some kind of resin-imbued Middle-Eastern-derived cloth!!]

1/28/14

Walking along a street. One one side a just-completed brick high school, An almost monumental building. On the other side, backyards of tenement housing. A two-story porch, sagging, screening torn and flapping in the wind,. One the first floor a woman is trying to use a typewriter, but the screen keeps blowing in her face,.

A broad landing of a staircase. An elderly woman in dressing gown is adjusting the position of drapes over the window and we comment on our shared aesthetic that everything has to be perfectly matched, left-to-right – drapes, and other.

A river runs under the bridge I cross. On the left is a huge, empty, factory complex clearly resembling Hopedale Mass. But on the other side of the bridge I'm in northern Framingham, Ma. But beyond the end of the street onto which I turn, the view is a little Bay in Lynn, Ma complete with the usual crowd of moored boats.

I've received a check realize with great anxiety that after paying the mortgage and one other bill, I'll be overdrawn.

At the beginning of a broad entry drive to where a sports arena is being built in the distance. There's only the bowl-shaped depression excavated so far and surrounding crests of earth into which lower level seats will be formed from concrete. Down from the crest of one region, access ramps descend to the drive. The are an exact configuration, much enlarged, of the channels that return bowling balls to from the pin area.

Beside me beside a road I notice it. A fat blue bird? For some reason it seems to be viciously preying on something beneath it, perhaps an insect? But something is strange about it and when I reach down to touch, I realize it's only a rock.

From the basement level of a ramshackle warehouse-type building a crowd pours, running, shouting, tussling. Some wear burqas, some men head and face coverings, others western clothing, I notice bare feet. Something about this mob has to do with their imperfect French spelling, including on billboards (such as one up on the building).

I've flown her in a Piper Cub that my daughter (who surely isn't a pilot or owner of an airplane in reality) has loaned me. The woman I've flown is elderly, and before the flight a man affiliated with some church-run senior citizen facility has informed me: how considerate the woman is. She will not fly if she's constipated. We've reached our destination and landed on a broad sandy strip beside a desolate lake. On the left there's an unoccupied old two-lane highway. She and I are pushing the plane along, making sure that the wings don't protrude over the highway, just in case a vehicle comes along. She doesn't want to take off, for she's become constipated. She explains that the disorder is due to excessive colonic absorption of moisture. We look for a place for her to hide try to defecate, but by the abrupt end of the segment of dream she's refused to cooperate.[thankfully, constipation has nothing to do with me in reality – nor flying.].

[in reality] I've just agreed to have a phone land-line installed (only $4 per mo. More than my "bundle" cost for internet and cable with Comcast. But I suddenly realize that my cell is sufficient. Perhaps I should call Comcast and see if I can make a trade: forget the phone but give me another Cable channel (Nature or Geographic or something).

That wakes me up. My only immediate need at 4 AM is to take a leak.

1/30/14

A bathroom with a slanting floor and otherwise evidence of ruination. I'm to remove the sink. I've already dug into the plaster and released it from the wall, but now I must tear up some of the flooring to disconnect pipes. Some young woman is watching me.

It seems like I've circled several blocks in Malden, MA, but then climbed to the top of a hill. I'm driving my old Toyota pickup truck. I start racing down the hill along with other cars, most of which turn on a side street. I realize that they've done so to avoid the usual tie-up at the downtown Medfield intersection ahead. But I continue straight down, pass under a railroad bridge which is in South Boston and the (actual situation) traffic light that suddenly comes into view turns yellow. Taking a chance, I run it.

It resembled route 16 through Wellesley and Holliston. Winding 2-lane road with expensive houses back behind extensive yards. I'm on my way to a medical appointment? Suddenly I see, about 6 feet high and wrapped in heavy plastic, a pile of cut-up logs. Realizing I can burn them in the woodstove, I pull over abruptly, but past the pile. I drive up over the front lawn which is the size of a field. At the far end toward which I back there's something covered with a tarp. And to my horror I've backed up against it. But I see no damage. But I find it impossible to get anywhere near the wood.

Resembling north Quincy Squantum area, but also Plum Island, parts of Scituate, as if "impression-collage" is the area I'm next in,. I can see the ocean just beyond the flat expanse that's occupied by very close-set structures. Some of them are 2-story, others mere cottage-size. All are kicked-out, windows, even frames missing, holes in walls, in roofs. As I drive in and out of the little streets and around behind it, one little building has had a fire, thus the roof-hole,. But people are living in it. [As I write this, I realize the whole area and condition resembles sections of New Orleans after the hurricane].

But then I'm on my way up route 28 in Reading, MA. I've just left the truck terminal where my old GMC cab-over tractor is parked on a steep embankment. It seems I'm supposed to use it to deliver a trailer somewhere, but I have to get oil. On I drive Northward. The street becomes a road becomes a trail becomes ruts and then I'm driving up and over tree roots and rocks and finally come to where (with others) there's no possibility to continue. I turn around and suddenly, back in the middle of Reading square, I've parked behind a automotive parts business. Inside, at the counter, I'm purchasing the gallons of oil.

But the delivery I'm next actually making is not with a tractor-trailer. It's some large container attached to the roof racks on my car. On the freight is huge lettering. I'm informed that not only am I transporting, but the while of the trip, I'm advertising whatever it is I'm carrying. I depart for my destination, and leaving the pickup locale I notice the cliff towering straight up behind the building.

2/3/14

It's a sprawling ranch house on an overgrown and littered yard. Seems to be in the center of Malden, MA, a small city I lived in when I was little. A couple partners and I have a contract to clean the place out and get it ready for the buyers to move into – quite soon.

The interior is a disaster. The front living room is partially filled with fallen insulation and other debris. Behind it is a room filled partly to the ceiling with all kinds of boxes and bags, the only contents really obvious being large sheets of thick plate glass that are too heavy for me to lift.

The floor of another room is half covered with thick, soiled shag carpet, its other half with cement, somewhat to the level of the shag fibers. The division between the surfaces is a kind of zig-zag.

Beside that room, the rear half of the chamber's floor seems to have been ripped (or rotted) away, including the joists. Part of the stone foundation below can be seen.

Walls of the rooms are covered with graffiti and mold.

Alone, I've started removing some of the debris. One of my partners shows up and I stress how soon we have to have the place ready for the owners. But his concern is to go across the street and get a large pepperoni pizza.

I go back inside, try to pull a piece of carpet from off a bed in the living room, but my late wife Angie is lying on the bed and has the carpet partially wrapped around her. I find it impossible.

Suddenly I'm in a 3' or so diameter storm-drain pipe that (actually did) runs under Upham Street in Melrose, MA. After fifty feet or so, this reached a catch basin under the edge of the street, a square manhole grate atop. I'm having fun until I look back in the pipe and realize a 3' diameter spider is following me. I scream through the grate for my adolescent friends to find a way to pull it loose so I can escape.

Back at the ranch house, nothing to speak of has been accomplished, my partners only concerned with pepperoni pizza But in the final, vague, scenario, I'm standing with either the realtor or owner of the place and quite amicably negotiating to receive complete payment.

2/6/14

It's a corridor in an office building. Bland, gray walls, floor, and it seems the consensus of those unseen with me that something needs to be done to such spaces. And suddenly the walls are embellished and decorated with images from the staged Lion King: African masks, carvings, panorama paintings – and various other motifs and objects of art from other inspirations.

Crossing a yard between rambling, old, frame two-family houses. Angie's with me as we negotiate our way over not just a strew of huge plastic rubbish bags. Here and there they're piled. But we reach the back porch of one of the houses, climb a set of stairs, enter, and climb further to the second floor. There, one of Angie's nieces is going to do our taxes.

And suddenly Angie and I are lying together, her back against me. She takes my arm and pulls it around her over her chest, grasping my hand tenderly. But the magic moment is over when we're walking along a street with modest late 9th century homes separated by generous yards of grass or shrubs. We consider the Victorian touches on porches, cornices: brackets, spindles, columns.

All the way at the end of the street she's no longer with me. And there, a tiny house is close to the street. It seems about one-bedroom size, with flat roof. Thus perhaps a "manufactured" unit. I realize that's where I'll reach the completion of my life and I feel secure and fulfilled.

2//24'14

In a waiting room of some medical practitioner. It's more like a retail store with plate glass windows looking out onto a small city street. Son Greg, about med. School age, is sitting in one of the chairs, either asleep or meditating or praying. But suddenly he jumps up and dashes out the door, clutching his chest. From his shirt pocket a squirrel is frantically trying to escape.

After a few minutes, my wife, Angie, suddenly beside me in the place, says I should go out and check on Greg. But outside, I find myself at the bottom a ramp down from the opposite side of the street to a parking lot below and behind the buildings. Trying to get to Greg, I walk up the ramp, now in fast-running water up to my chest.

Then in a cavernous warehouse into which a couple tractor trailer rigs are backed. From one of them the pallets of large white bags (plastic pellets?) are being unloaded. The warehouse floor level is some thirty feet above the truck's floor, and a unique forklift is being used. It's blades descend down to the truck, the raise the pallets one at a time to the height of the warehouse floor. As I watch the unloading I chat with a couple other drivers and a dispatcher, who tells me that unfortunately there are no opportunities for me to work sporadically on interstate trips.

Having left that building I'm with grandson Vincent, about early teen-age. We've driven all the way (3 hours) from Boston to Portland, Maine on our way to the annual summer camping trip (that I actually shared with his father long, long before. Suddenly Vincent tells me that he's forgotten to bring his sleeping bag and other paraphernalia absolutely necessary for camping. This means we have to drive all the way back to Boston . . . where I find myself in the trucking warehouse again and the dispatcher has me going to on a run to Quincy to pick up a load of household goods. A woman is moving out of her premises. The freight is palletized and he hopes that if I bring a pallet jack I'll be able to just roll it out of the building into the trailer.

And as suddenly I'm in an essentially vacated apartment with my wife, Angie. For some reason as she busies herself with the contents of kitchen cabinets I'm just standing, neglected. Angered, I start lecturing her about how many times she'd typically berate me for being busy and not paying attention to her and now she 's doing it to me. Adult son, Jack, appears and I find myself outside for we've all wondered what the temperature is. Both thermometers show nothing but blacked behind their lenses (one rectangular, the other round). Across the side lawn I see that all the fascia and soffit and some other trim has been removed from our neighbor's house.

2/26/`14

My wife, Angie, and I are on foot, crossing Main St. in downtown Malden, Ma. We're in good spirits, on our way to dine out. But suddenly she's harassing me about doing nothing for her and not caring and only thinking of myself . . and on and on every complaint imaginiable – none of which apply to me. Especially at that moment considering that we've been out somewhere for the evening and now I'm taking her to dinner.

Suddenly we're in a stark tenement apartment. There's no furniture. She's still complaining, accusing, in-my-face to the point that I'm experiencing overwhelming frustration. I slam a door, bang my head against the flaking plaster of a wall. But she keeps on ranting until I start to rush out of the place, stating that "I just can't take this shit anymore."

But there appears another woman and who seems to be superimposing counseling procedures. And finally Angie quiets, looks sheepish, and makes a comment about acting-out when she's had too much to drink. The woman mentions something about it also could be related to bleedting. B l e e d T i n g. All three of us laugh, and somewhat in unison state the word and spell it correctly (without the T).

I'm elsewhere. I'm looking down from a second floor window. Across a yard, from the second floor a steady stream of mostly young women is descending an outside staircase and streaming off across the yard. I realize I too need to urinate.

On the side of a desolate stretch of old two lane highway. Surrounded by a 3 foot or so high granite wall had been some grand building. All that remains of it is foundation filled with rubble and debris. But at the four corners tall columns still stand, giving me the impression that I'm looking at a desecrated mosque whose minarets (though Doric columns) are still intact.

Suddenly it's night and I'm outside the granite wall. From the roadway I'm shoveling a strew of gravel that has fallen off of trucks entering the property during the day. I'm dressed in white pajamas, but still a bit concerned whether I'd be seen by any vehicle coming along. But the road is vacant in the dismal dark of the night. I look both ways and continue kind of swishing the gravel off the pavement with the shovel.

And suddenly it's daylight and someone is with me. At the edge of the road where I'd been pushing the gravel there's now a pile of massive tree limbs, pieces of structure, rubbish, dressed stone blocks, and more. I'm explaining that the disposal truck will be able to back right up to the pile – but that the granite and any architectural remnants must be saved so that they can go to a museum or be retained on site.

My unseen colleague and I have walked on down to the drive that enters the other side of the property. These narrow passages, each between a pair of carved granite gate posts integral with the granite wall, curve together onto the weed-infested and ruined remains of what had been a paved courtyard in front of the foundation. Many children are playing in this area. Bordering the front of the area are stone slabs, each perhaps 8 feet high by twice that width, and carved with symbols and scenarios, some including chariots.

But now there seems to be a standing building where only the corner pillars and foundation had been. I'm on the second floor of that building, having rushed up there to urinate. I'm familiar with the place. For one thing, though there's no window now to see outside, I realize that from that very locale I'd previously looked across the yard at the girls going down the stairway. And now as I pee in the toilet I realize that although it had to have been there all along, I'd never noticed the urinal that another buy has hurriedly approached and was now using.

Finished together, as we walk to the staircase down he mentions knowing something about some relative of mine who had experienced a blood pressure aberrance that related to a urinary constriction. The guy tells me that the reason he wants to know is that he only urinates twice a day (at most). I'm just about to ask him "what the hell's your blood pressure then? About 50/30 – 10?"

But he's gone and I'm out the desecrated courtyard or plaza. With me is an interior designer with whom (and for whom) I'd done décor work years and years ago. We're considering the various antique mantles and carved woodwork and pieces of furniture that the children have set up like displays here and there on the pitted and cracked paving stones.

The woman and I agree. Yes, there's a market for that kind of material.

[Concerning the above: during the previous two days I'd read a history of Egypt from 3500 BCE to the present. Thus the instigation of ruins, minaret/columns at corners, and carved pictoral stone panel.

A week ago, due to heavy snowfall I'd shoveled off the roof of my trailer home. Thus, though "kaleidoscoped", the black roof material became the black of night and road in the dream – my white pajamas combining snow and Egyptian traditional clothing – gravel as snow.

The first segment with my wife "off the wall at me" is cathartic-remembrance of those troubled times past. And from back in that era the interior decorator woman and "architectural antiques" (mantles etc.) and marketing such materials. . . .which I did in using them in my own décor designs and simply selling the stuff to a couple dealers.]

2/27/14

Sooty, shaling concrete walls, ceiling, floor. The deteriorated industrial realm extending into the distance somewhat like passageway. But it's the interior of a labyrinth of such concrete-walled sections of various size in a monstrous building. In this chamber, on both sides of a metal table of great length, Hispanic men and women are engaged in preparing salads.

I'm noticed and approached by their supervisor, a round-faced and pot-bellied very swarthy man. He's grinning broadly and seems friendly. So I have no reservations in asking him where, in the building complex, I'll find the recruiting office.

He walks me to where the floor level of the salad enterprise drops off four feet or so to a ramp that slopes on downward and into the oblivion beyond. We jump down onto the ramp and approach a heavily damaged 1960s vintage auto body (no wheels) that's on a big freight dolly. The smiling man kicks a chock from under the dolly wheel and gives a push and the thing careens down the ramp and away.

"Recruiteeng office that way, senor," he tells me.

But I find myself at the corner of a very flat field, perhaps 3 acres, enclosed by chain link fence. All around are tenement and three-decker houses, a slum-like scenario. And suddenly I'm in the corner room of a building that's at the corner of the lot where I'd been standing. My back is against a garage door that now shuts the opening through the side wall.of the structure. To my right is another garage door on the opening through the rear wall.

My hand on his shoulder, I'm telling advising a middle-aged man. He's just finished telling me his frustration with his teenage children who run up the phone and light bills that he has to pay.

I advise him that through the door behind me he should make them appear to collect a specific amount of allowance. And then they should be required to go to the rear door and, according to some proportion of the utility bills which would be based on a fraction of their average ages and of the sum of his and his wife's.

Back in the concrete building's decrepit but definitely busy interior. Resembling a combination of old factory and sloppy auto repair facility and receiving area of a rubbish incinerator is the realm of rooms, small ones off at angles here and there, and I in a huge central one with towering ceiling. Around me therein are machines that all seem inoperative, steel drums containing and overloaded with metallic pieces and parts, fragments and fractions of things indiscernable everywhere inbetween and on top of each other and all else. Many people seem to be laborers within the area, though there's no evidence of what they could be laboring at. Certainly not organizing the place.

But I see a ramp up. And as I approach it I see about a 4' wall. And atop it, on into a concrete walled hallway I walk on the concrete floor. "Recruiting Office?" I ask someone who walks by me. "Keep going."

I see the door with "Recruiting Office" stenciled on it.

But closer, it's the door of the crumpled car body on the dolly that the round-faced Hispanic guy had pushed. I open the door. Inside, yes, there's a desk at which a young man in military uniform is seated. But for me to confer with him, I have to climb into the car body and lie atop the mattress-like strew of clothing and curtains and rugs and table cloths.

Lying thereon, I'm comfortable, he's courteous and attentive to my inquiry about joining up.

But suddenly, in unison, we're saying "The military always needs *good* men, but at 75 years, "*old*" is the determinant terminology."

[the concrete building images are from a composite of sources: movie scenes, warehouse interiors to which I delivered freight, and especially some 40 years ago a building in Boston wherein I designed and built a cocktail lounge. The fenced land amid the tenements was a parcel in occupied by its original colonial home and carriage house and owned by a dealer of architectural antiquities to whom I sold scavenge and demolition way back. Hispanics, round faces, car body on dolly are all image-fragments all but untraceable. As for the recruiting office – before retiring for the night and the above dream I'd watched the DVD "War Horse"

3/5/14

First, behind me is an expanse that resembles a school athletic field or park but with no details of image. Bordering it on one side in front of me is an abrupt elevation, perhaps twenty feet high, which stretches off to both sides, completely level. Side by side atop this embankment are little buildings which, about one-room size. As I dream I realize there's some connection between these tiny structures and the desolate houses along the road way, way back in my "valley of the flies" dream. But here, the sheds or shacks seem cheery, a couple constructed from branches and twigs.

Beside me a busy street. Under me the brick-paved sidewalk I'm to repair. There's a small sunken area in which water collects. I've already placed curbing along each side of the area and am about to obtain some plaque or other feature to place in the center of the hot-top I'll use to fill the depression. But I notice that a crack has just developed, kind of a microcosmic grand canyon on through the sidewalk and out onto the street. The water from the depressed area is nicely draining and I won't have to do anything.

Driving beside a semblance of part of Boston harbor. A wreck of a tug boat is pushing another derelict-looking craft. The latter suddenly achieves its own power and pulls away from the tug. In the dream I'm amused at dreaming the fusion imagery of boats . . .and a motor vehicle getting a jump-start by being pushed.

Turning away from the water, I'm in an extremely decrepit motor vehicle with unseen others. We turn off the street (which resembles lower Summer St. in Boston) and are all but tunneling under such a complex of steel framework for something being built. Part of the planned structure seems to be a ramp that will descend into the water. Emerging from under the beams and cross-members and mesh and all, the area is an expanse of harbor-front land on which a whole warehouse complex has been torn down.

At the far end of this rubble-rumpled spread I find myself trying to keep three long rolls of some kind of roofing material on a two-wheel hand-truck. They're needed on the other side of the barren where something is to be built. But I see nothing and the rolls tip off but I'm being helped by Bill [in actuality a dispatcher from my job who died at least 15 years ago].

It seems that I'm still in this above region, but in a long alley. On one side there's a wall against which is a banquette (or bench) with padded back. It stretches all along from one end to the other of the alley. On the other side is the rear of a one story building, trash here, broken window patched there, bent bars securing a rear entry here and there – desolate.

But through one rear door that's in good shape there's a window. And as I'm direc ted (by someone) to look through it, it seems that inside there's some kind of meeting hall or senior center. Along the one wall I can see, people are seated on a bench. Over their heads are pictures on the wall. Someone I can't see has been lecturing or preaching,and regarding God, one woman seated at the wall shakes her head and comments that she doesn't think God Himself would believe such ideas. A few people away, an elderly man is laughing in response.

3/10/14
A small vacant lot in which I'm sitting behind the wheel of a tractor-trailer rig. But then I see through the window that I'm surrounded by pews, as if I'm in a rig inside a church. No people, though.

Next, driving out of the lot I come onto a street going uphill. It turns abruptly right and has become a kind of corridor within a crowded restaurant. Many others are moving along with me, and it seems questionable whether I'm going to be able to make the sharp right considering the length of the trailer I'm pulling. I may end up knocking over a table or two.

Two men, apparently gay, are fastened to a wall. They're being interviewed in some kind of TV event. The interviewer is harassing them, but apparently from his also gay insider-status. There is no actual subject or context revealed in the dream, but at the end of this brief segment all three men are almost convulsed with laughter.

I'm carrying an armful of large-pizza-size cartons of something or other. On top of them is a little terrier dog. I'm approaching my residence and very concerned how I'm going to be able to unlock the door without dropping the dog.

A desolate railroad crossing. It seems that I'm on foot and need to get somewhere but there are no indications of where I am or to where I'm to go. A freight comes along, box cars, tanks, then three steam locomotives on a flatbed car, then more box cars. The rate of travel slows considerably and I realize that the train is ascending to the higher elevation of Shirley and then on into Fitchburg. I consider that I might be able to catch a ride, but two factors dissuade me from even moving toward the freight cars. One is that it's actually moving faster than it seems, in that it's slowed down from its original rate – and were I to try to grab hold of something on a car, my arms might get pulled off. Two is that the car I'd jump on would be toward the end of the train. Thus, by the time it would be passing through Shirley (where I'd want to get off), the rest of the consist would have attained a rather level stretch and have accelerated. I might get killed trying to jump off!!

Someone whose face is obviously red even in the night TV camera's light, is being interviewed. The program will air the following morning. Something embarrassing has taken place No details. But the matter has to be dealt with in advance of broadcast, so this night-time filming allows rehearsal, so to speak.

[regarding the last segment, I'd watched a documentary in which many people were interviewed, some of them in semi-dark situations. As for all the earlier dream content, just fragments, a kind of collage of image and context – the pizza-box size cartons probably actual pizza-box images, the little dog seen in a car that passed me a couple days before, Etc. etc.]

From the road, a view down onto an expanse of old industrial buildings. I drive down and through an area of the three and four story brick structures, turn onto a street of decrepit Victorian houses, and park. As I walk up the street I pick up something, assuming it's being thrown out. On aways, I'm just about to grab another curb-side something that I realize will form a system with what I've already picked. Just as I'm about to grasp it, from around a telephone pole a short, black man sort of plummets to the ground, striking his head. He gets up, others gather around him and me, and after some discussion it's amiably resolved that he's not throwing the object away, he realizes I didn't know this, and as far as his fall, he's alright. But the others and I make him aware that on his forehead there's a rather large swelling.

A type of pine tree with very long, horizontal branches is growing in a basement area where construction is taking place. A woman who was attempting to break off a branch seems to have suffered a heart attack. She's been carried out of the cellar by means of a rough removal of part of the foundation wall and some excavation beyond. The construction is to be an egress and stairs.

A city street with store-fronts, many of them wide open to the sidewalk. The area is crowded, music is blaring out of some interiors some of which are very dimly lit, or have strings of lights around the entries, or hanging tassels and mobiles and such. I'm in one where I seem to know others, one of whom is a girl who very much appears to be a lamp. She sees me and disappears.

I'm led out of there by someone who's telling me that "flat-top" is well known in the area *["the area" in ways reminiscent of the "combat zone" of bars and strip joints that used to be in Boston]*. Flat-top seems to have been my next-door neighbor when I lived in Franklin, MA. Into another of these noisy dives I'm being ushered upstairs. The owner there is the image of the most crazed character in the movie, Good Fellas. But he's friendly, intimating something to me about any friend of Flat Top is a friend of his.

3/11/14

A narrow street, some pedestrians, storefronts, a couple with tables and chairs on the sidewalk. European-looking place. Crossing under the street is a canal, as if in a chasm between buildings. From the sidewalk a ramp down to a walkway alongside the water. I walk my bike down and soon lean it against the basement-level wall of a building. As I look at the support of the road over the canal I see that it's the same stone and steel construction used for a railroad track to cross over a road. I feel a hand on my shoulder, turn, and a priest, somewhat annoyed, is telling me that in parking my bike I've knocked his shirt to the ground. I turn, see, and point out to him that what he thinks is his shirt is just a white plastic bag.

At an inlaws back door. It's early morning. A woman delivering magazines has just emerged and the door's almost shut as go to enter. I announce my presence, the door opens wide, and I'm welcomed in. But the specific person I've come to see has gone for a bike ride with her neighbor. I'll have to wait.

And while I wait I'm involved with unseen others in removing some very large piece of equipment *[nuclear or other warfare == from DVD documentary I'd watched before sleeping?]* up from the basement. We struggle the thing across a collapsing back porch floor and are most thankful to see that stretching beyond is the remains of a railroad trackbed – the rails have been removed, but the ties are still in place.

3/20/14

At least a foot of snow on the ground. I'm on one side of a park or athletic field surrounded by a chain link fence about 8' high. Beyond the fence on the far side there are either garden apartment buildings or dormitories. It seems I'm supposed to get over there, But there's no indication of any means of my doing so (no vehicle, not even a sense of my being a body which could walk through the snow and cold). At the corner of the fence at the corner of a thorofare onto which the street I've been on intersects, the dream just ends.

3/25/14

An upward-inclining avenue with decrepit, even slum-like, storefronts and other commercial structures on each side. Dismal, depressing, but I continue on. I'm on a bike. Which has suddenly brought me inside a massive equipment repair facility. The dispatcher from my previous job [actuality] makes a brief appearance to instruct me that I have to deliver something or other all the way up to the end of the Avenue.

I note that the conveyance (no longer a bike) seems to be a cluster of pipes bolted together, this sort of demented roof-rack configuration mounted on a truck chassis. As it moves with me clinging to the pipes, I wonder if I'll be thrown off onto the street.

But I'm on a bike again, now pedaling off the avenue and down an inclined drive beside what could either be an 19th century brick factory building or a church. Through shattered windows in the walls I observe that construction is going on inside. At the end of the building I turn behind it, and at the other side emerge onto a massive space surrounded, afar, by other similar factory buildings. The ground itself slopes as if a flattened funnel, downward away from me. It's evident that part of the parcel had once had buildings upon it, outlines of foundations now filled-in with rubble evident somewhat like crossword puzzle configurations [deriving from a DVD documentary on crosswords I'd watched a few nights prior] . . . . other areas paved with concrete slabs, granite, brick parquetry, and tar.

Although I'd pedaled downhill from the avenue and around the back of the building, now I'm on the bike and coasting dangerously fast down the incline of this domain of demolition . .. toward where it exits between brick walls with iron gates . . onto the avenue.

Again, I'm pedaling slowly up the Ave. I come to a sudden perspective of a harbor below where the roadway suddenly stops with no barrier, no bridge ahead. [this "flash-scenario" from a prior dream complete with details of vessels on the water below and misplaced locks (as if in a canal)].

The avenue doesn't seem to end – rather, it frays off into several driveways or trails through rubbish and detritus, disposals, etc. At first I'm concerned, but have no way to call back to the dispatcher who has sent me here.

Then I notice a gouged and rusted commercial roll-up door opening onto a partially destroyed cement garage building. I feel relief, reassurance. And soon, from within, a chain kind of slinks along the ground and out and then, attached to it there emerge a pair of huge German shepherd dogs except they are also leopards from their shoulder-hip regions downward. Their spots are brilliant on their bellies as they roll and tussle with each other.

From the blackness behind the opened door staggers an epic extreme of derelict-drunk, his soiled clothes seemingly slathered on his body and spittles bejeweling his snarled facial hair.

He notices my concerned scrutiny of the dog-leopards.

"No worry," he proclaims in high British enunciation. "They're gentle as lambs."

3/29/14

I'm on an old highway bordered by desolate steppe-like expanses. I proceed, ever upward, finally coming to the summit [which very much resembles what you see when you've left route 128 at the circle and come uphill to the statue in Gloucester]. Although there's the subliminal awareness that I have also reached a somewhat Tibetan pinnacle, as I look around I see streets spoking from where I'm at. And on each side of the streets are inner-city (three-decker dwellings, storefronts, etc) structures.

I'm supposed to deliver the load in my rig to an antique, wood-frame hotel (think the Mt.Washington Hotel in N.H., or the one in the movie, "The Shining"). But it's nowhere to be seen. I ask several people, one who's outside a barbershop that's atop a set of stairs from the street. This African man has no idea where the hotel is, though he knows it's in the area and famous.

A couple other nondescript people (one at an intersection) say the same thing. I'm already a little concerned that there was a delivery appointment time, now passed.

Suddenly, from the intersection, I'm transported to what looks like scale-model Alpine terrain – peaks and crevasses, I on high but plummeting down into a cirque or crease but it's not rocky realm I'm in. Either sand or warm snow is what I slide down on, finding myself in a concrete-paved expanse between partially wrecked factory buildings.

I ride a bike into one.

Everyone (unseen) therein knows of the hotel but has no idea where it is. And now it seems like several hours have passed and I haven't made the delivery (time-sensitive freight) and there's no way I can phone my dispatcher.

And then I find myself in a flat field of many acres. On one side it's bordered by a high chain-link fence with razor wire atop. With me it seems are several college-age people, also looking for a way out of the field. I realize as I walk along the fence, that on the other side of it is the highway which I'd traveled significantly uphill -- but now it seems, like the field, to be horizontal.

We come to the remains of a structure against the fence, window and door frames kicked-out, partitions partially punctured. There's no way out of the field, so we depart to continue our search until cows, a lot, are noticed ahead. We turn back. We come to a gate now in the fence. At least I emerge from confinement in the field.

But I've emerged not onto the highway. I'm in a cavernous, desecrated industrial building, its floor at basement level but the ceiling height that of a first floor above ground level. It seems that I and my small college-age crew (perhaps those from the field?) are supposed to rebuild the interior of this space with some kind of décor. Wood paneling is involved. Metal plates on the walls have to be removed first. And other unspecified, but overwhelming, demolitions and removals will be required. As in other dreams, in this dream I'm dreaming (along with the scenario) a realization that I'm dreaming about a situation (or dimension) of my life in which I'm involved in something over my head, an overwhelming undertaking that I may not be up to fulfilling.

But along with a black guy I first pull out some sections of piping from a wall, and we're about to remove the wall to thus encompass everything in one space – but I interrupt our endeavors, telling him I have to pee.

At which point I wake up

3/30/14

Crossing Main Street in Malden where I lived when I was a very young boy. I seem to be with a woman, likely my mother, but unseen. But it's clear what I'm telling her (though there's no sound of my voice in the dream).

In reality, at the age I would have been in the dream (with my mother), there had been a Boston Edison generating plant in a fairly small brick building right on Main Street a short distance down from where we're crossing it. Some years later, obsolete, the equipment was moved out and the building became the home of Bluestein, The Office People, a prototype of our era's Staples or Office Depot. Bluestein thrived for awhile, but didn't survive to proliferate beyond the one building. And at the time in the dream, the building would still have been Boston Edison.

But I'm telling my mother that I'd considered dropping in to see the Bluesteins and tell them how fondly I remembered being in their store some years before.

And I'm suddenly by myself in a narrow passage, somewhat resembling a hospital corridor but actually (in the dream) a store, but empty of any commodities. I hear someone moaning and realize that the sound, combining agony and ecstasy, is due to the administration of a barium enema.

Driving a flat-bed truck, pretty decrepit. I'm on an unpaved passage that arcs between empty lots strewn with shipping detritus and parts, and one-story buildings that are probably for storage, but look as if they've been abandoned for ages. Partly crushed, collapsed, and otherwise mangled chain link fence borders the area, beyond which I sense is Boston Harbor.

Along comes a friend and former partner of mine from at least forty years ago. But in the dream he's the age he was then. With him in the pickup truck he's driving, are two women that I realize are his wives. We're both parked in the middle of the passage and decide to back over so that, though unlikely, someone else on the road would be able to drive past us.

With great difficulty including jumping up and down on it, he manages to open the hood of his vehicle and, immediately, closes it, only achieving that by again jumping up and down.

But he and I are then walking in a neat park which resembles the Esplanade area next to the Charles River in Boston. The river is visible in the distance, but in a direction that would have the Boston park on the other side, in Cambridge.

As we walk I'm looking up at the sky. There, in amazing detail, are a male and female figure dressed in leisure clothing, almost photographic apparitions of what I mention to my friend must be images of department store clothing display dummies. But, as I dream, I dream that I'm dreaming (but not telling him) that I realize what

I'm seeing is only dream-imagery – for in the sky one may see substantive suggestion in the cloud formations, but not photographic accuracies, certainly not actualities.

Looking up again I see a small airplane, very high, heading North, then another, lower, and I wonder which one is being piloted by a co-worker-truck-driver of mine before I retired last year. I sense a longing to be able to fly off into the distance.

3/31/14

I'm with my wife, Angie, and unseen others in a car. We've left some kind of gathering or discussion somewhere, having decided we need go to the big city for our safety. We're now on a highway and although I think I recognize scenic familiarity to outskirts of Baltimore, I'm informed that we're approaching Illinois [probably Chicago, for I was born there and during the last week have been trying to obtain immunization records].

We're at quite an elevation, the land undulating impressively around us. On one side, beyond a valley area, there's an immense farm-building complex that I point out to Angie. On the right, similar sinuous fields but studded with industrial complexes and, apparently, some office parks.

Into the labyrinth of super-highways entering the city but having only glimpsed an overhead signboard for upcoming exits, suddenly we're off on an old two-lane road. We're now going through an old, tenement and industrial area that's suggestive of a previous dream's itinerary.

That we need to get gas is a sudden panic for me. It seems the gauge showed empty when we 'd set-off. But when I've stopped beside the pumps at a station, I notice that it now shows that we have over half a tank. In the dream I think, "reality should be so replenishing!"

Then, without connecting content, we've arrived at an upstairs apartment. A number of people are there including Angie, some of the truck drivers from my job, the wife of an old high school friend who also seems to be one of my nieces, and one of the dock workers from my job.

We're just about to have a turkey dinner. The women are carving. The truck drivers and dock worker, though there before, now seem to arrive by coming upstairs. The old high school friend has just gotten out of a bed, and he's complaining to me about his privacy now destroyed and his dislike of the group entering the apartment.

I mention to him that sometimes it's anyone that destroys another's privacy – even someone that, the night before, you couldn't wait to get into bed with (and into) who, the next morning, you can't stand the presence of !!

The dock worker starts to engage my old friend in some heated discussion. Friend announces he's had it, he's leaving, and despite my intervention to calm and console, he goes down the stairs.

That leaves the rest of us upstairs ready to dine on the turkey. The rest of us is now only three people.

Friend's wife/niece and I determine that we should set plates on the buffet, rather than on the mattress. The buffet is the embellished Victorian sideboard that had been in my family for three generations. She's put the bone China plates on the top. I've opened the silverware drawer, advising her not to pull it out too far or it'll drop to the floor. But the silverware sections are in so far that we decide it's necessary to break off the divisions between them and the outer part of the drawer. In so doing, we seem to be somewhat desecrating the valuable piece of furniture, defiling its aesthetic antiquity. But now the access to the implements is just a matter of sliding things.

4/1/14

At first I've walked across an expanse of grass, probably a park, a come to a low retaining wall. I jump up to the higher level. A young man, apparently a college student, is slumped on a wide stairway leading up to a dormitory or administration building, I surmise. He watches me critically, as I'm doing some kind of intricate footwork as I proceed.

I'm on a cement walkway which stretches on into the distance. There's a strong suggestion of the Esplanade in Boston, but up toward Mass Ave where the lawn, through which a walk extends, is narrow.

Definitely there's a body of water to my right. But it's at the foot of a rather steep and strewn embankment. To my left there's the back of a ramshackle industrial building with a large delivery door opening almost adjacent to the walk. Upon the plank floor of the place, stacked between beams which form the frame of the door, I'm unloading a number of cans containing leaking paint or some other rather viscous chemical. I place the cans on their sides, a can of the second tier high "nesting" between two on the first tier.

Then I'm walking inside the building and looking for someone to sign for my delivery. Although there seems to be a great deal of activity around me, I see no one. But I'm informed (somehow) that because it's right after Christmas, work is so slow that the winter vacation has resulted in most everyone being laid off. As I walk through an area full of industrial woodworking and milling machinery it seems that I'm the only one who's not on leave.

An extremely tall man passes me. He's wearing shorts and has knee-high stockings. Before I can speak he's gone down a long flight of stairs. I follow and am able to inform him that I've delivered the cans. He and another man, both supervisors, I assume, approve my having left the delivery of cans as I have. But I'm instructed to be sure that the big overhead door is closed, thus the cans contained securely within the building, before I leave.

A second brief segment. I'm in the military, perhaps. But the locale seems to be part of the above industrial building. Some young woman has been deviously attempting to advance her rank or position. No details, but after a traipse through factory and warehouse spaces full of clutter and partially destroyed machinery [images from Clinton, MA where I used to deliver to a warehouse full of very old plastic injection-molding equipment]. I finally come to a room rather full of people. They must be military, for she's among them.

I take a place with the group at a round table and am lecturing the woman about her impropriety in attempting subterfuge and inveigle as career and rank advancement ahead of another (me). I tell her on no uncertain terms that what she's done has had the result of alienation others, thus to her detriment.

"To forge ahead of the mere flow of procedure and command advancement, you have to endear yourself to those of influence, not challenge, appear an impediment, or flaunt your singular assumptions of entitlement of superiority."

My having stated this "in her face", so to speak, I must have catharted something about someone, for the dream has suddenly ended.

4/2/14

I'm in a vast, empty warehouse. It seems I'm supposed to meet someone there or attend a meeting. But it's just an empty space, low ceiling, concrete floor, and on one side a number closed delivery dock doors. [image from an actual warehouse in Wilmington, MA].

At the far end there's a sort of large cubicle, perhaps a "break room" or office area. Near it, I see several people inside, and my hair is suddenly frothed with shampoo suds which I need to get washed out. Behind the cubicle is another partitioned area with a sign designating "lavatory" over the entrance door. But I'm not sure whether it's a men's or women's facility.

And suddenly it seems that I'm on an upper level of the same building. A woman behind a desk is being good-naturedly scolded by a tax or business-practice inspector for not providing her employees with the necessary wage-level [this, from a book I'm reading on the exploitation of merchant marine seamen]. She protests, one of her arguments being that he's going to force her to have to pay her little dog.

As I observe their interaction, I recognize the man and tell him I admire greatly what he has done for humanity. He looks pleased, but curious. I tell him that I've seen is pictures in various sources.

He continues his discussion with the woman and I wander to the other side of the office where there's a bin on the floor in which people leave things for the needy *[there's a small one in my local library]*. I notice the only contents are all kinds of shoes [a couple days prior I'd taken a walk in a mall where there were four shoe stores].. Most of those in the bin were of the Nike or Adidas variety ("sneaker-like), [such as my son was wearing when I was with him yesterday], but one pair of foot-ware that especially caught my eye was the fur-lined women's calf-high boots down at the bottom of the container.

[I awoke tumescent, though never having had a "foot fetish" fixation.]

.

Back to sleep.

I'm in a Volkswagen "beetle", stopped at a red light which turns green. But I'm either reading something or so engrossed in conversation with a passenger that I don't notice until horns are (silently) signaling other drivers' annoyance. [years ago I'd driven my son's VW across the country so he could have it in San Diego]. My passenger at the light had asked whether I'd ever been on a road trip and it seems I'd been telling her that "we're on one now".

Said son's wife and I are together (with unseen others, a gathering or audience or congregation) . I've just signed my name above the top printed line of a menu or church service handout – which was somehow related to my late wife. I begin to cry but am consoled when daughter-in-law asks what religion I was brought up in. She guesses Episcopalian. I tell her Congregational. She informs me that the Congregational denomination split off from some fundamentalist, and cruel, former sect which, as she told of it, seemed almost like the worst of Islam [I'm involved in editing a friend's recollections of being stationed in Iran years ago].

The chamber in which daughter-in-law (and the others) and I are in suddenly seems to be the interior of a church. The ceiling is very high above, perhaps arched. In front of us there's a wall of tall windows, mosaic glazing (though, as usual, no color). She's mentioning something about the persecution and torture of martyrs by the predecessor sanctity of Congregationalism when, before us has come to be ... picture the setup they have to display doors (or rugs) in a Home Depot – or for posters in another venue. The doors or other items are affixed on a rack by pins so that they can be "leafed-through", as if pages of a book.

Such a setup was now before us and the huge, window-size "pages" were like medieval paintings of religious scenes and suffering of persons involved. Regarding anyone's accepting such horrendous torture for not worshipping some deity rather than another, I express my opinion in no uncertain terms.

"I'd kneel down before whatever altar and verbalize (or enact) apparent worship of whatever deity demanded . . . .all the while in my heart and mind addressing to my Supreme Being conception/image. Agony unto self-destruction hardly seems like a part of any rational religion, conclude.

There follows a very hazy realization that I'm on another road trip, in a bus, and commenting to the person beside me (as we watch other passengers fighting and falling in the aisle) that my preference in the future will be to travel by rail. [and for some time I've actually been contemplating a cross-country Amtrak trip].

4/3/14

A very busy dream night.

First I'm inside what resembles a cathedral, or a shopping mall, Ahead and behind me stretches the enclosed space, its ceiling towering above. But it's also as if Mass. Avenue through the South End of Boston had been enclosed. For on each side are the facades of bow-front row-house buildings (also picture Back Bay or other citys' similar areas of adjacent buildings. In the dream, these facades at one point are identical to one area of Mass Ave, complete in detail to a "step-back" of the units.

I'm in one of the buildings, empty, not gutted but damaged and strewn. [many years ago I considered buying the property which is the origin of location and other description of the dream]. I'm going to have jack hammer part of the floor of a bathroom to access pipes to repair.

And suddenly I'm in an undulating field area, apparently beside some water way [here, Chelsea, Mass is the inspiration]. Around me are pieces and parts of vehicles and probably marine equipment. But my specific concern is reattaching a trailer hitch to my step-van. Along comes a man vaguely resembling the father of one of my high school friends, but also the loan shark of the second mortgage I once had to take out on my house.

He makes some comments about my predicament, for my truck and everything around is hardly beyond junk-state. So we set out on foot, carrying some tools, and find ourselves together in the cathedral/mall/Mass. Ave. scenario. We're going to collaborate on the repairs and renovations. Into a building we go, but I notice that there's a fresh repair patch in the bath floor. We step outside and someone reveals that we're in the wrong building, We're supposed to be in one with the step-back façade (which, as we approached along the street/nave/corridor was hidden by the building fronts closer to the street.

Inside the right building, back in the bath area, I open a small, wooden box fastened to the wall. It resembles what, if metal, might be an electrical equipment unit (such as fuse or breaker-box) or telephone wiring terminal box). But my comment is "we've come a long, long way in medicine cabinet design".

An brief interval of almost chaotic sequence comes next. It involves a big box of something and a dinner plate that's about four feet in diameter. I'm supposed to return these to the man who was with me in the building, but his home is high above and I'm finding it impossible to climb up over a pile of debris and disposal and partially demolished structure to get to his residence. And then I'm on a bike and then on foot in within a realm of windswept, dismal distance suggestive of scenery from *Wuthering Heights.* Then just a flash of being in a kitchen and returning the items to the guy and his wife.

But I'm back down in the Mass-Ave ménage. The step-back building façade is at the corner of the main street/nave/corridor and side-street/aisle perpendicular to it.[no question a significant "scavenge" of this configuration is from my having gone for a walk inside a nearby shopping mall].

But the "aisle" is just a short egress. And I'm outside. And back inside seems to be the interior of a college class building. And outside with me are a number of college age kids. Extending up over there's a pilaster, probably supporting cantilevered structure. Around this massive pole, like bands (each perhaps 4' high) are corrugated metal. Sections sagging, partially unwrapping themselves, and otherwise askew.

But, as if the pilaster were a roll of baked dough, I'm looking at just one "slice" of it that one of the students around me has insisted I take from him. It's morphed to a size I can hold in m hand and resembles a buttermilk biscuit. Around it there's no metal, but a sheet of paper kind of like a skirt (or picture a biscuit-with-paper below as a jelly fish). There's no writing on the paper. There's no sound in the dream. But it must be the student group chanting that inform me what the message and the meaning of all this is: Quakers worship Satan and there's no question the source of some of the ingredients of this idolatrous item prove that it's satanic. [only after waking and at this point of recording the dream do I realize that the connection here is *Quaker* Oats Corporation].

4/4/14

It seems like a medical facility waiting room. On a far wall is a large flat-screen TV showing something about some young boy. I'm seated next to a table, very similar to an actual one one of my sons owns. Unseen other people are with me.

A former co-worker (truck driver) comes into the place. He asks if we've heard. "Heard what?" "Diane Sawyer died." "She was too young." Is one reaction. I ask him what she died from.

His answer is "low sperm count".

Because the screen doors we've installed are imperfect, someone else and I are going to have to paint them in order to get paid. I contemplate how quickly this can be done without getting paint on the screen.

But I'm up on a ladder painting a gable above the doors, and the building seems to be a broad storefront across the old highway from a large field or marsh. Realizing that the upper areas are too high to be reached, I go back inside the building, down into a basement area.

There, I'm slouched on a couch between two other couches, the three in a straight line against a wall that seems to be in the same area as the waiting room, but not. On all three couches are other members of my family.

My wife, Angie, and I are in another place and she's found the attaché case in which I hide pornography. She seems bemused. I inform her that it's a "guy thing".

Back on the couch and someone hands me a CD which I don't play on anything, but, but am able to "read" my son Jack's recorded message. It's requesting that for my birthday I should make some kind of speech to everyone conveying how much they mean to me. I tell this to everyone.

And I tell them that in so many ways I've already told each of them how important they are to me, cherished by me. And, as far as telling them I love them, I tell them that in the past few years I've probably said "I love you" in various ways to the point of neurosis.

Everyone seems appreciatively in agreement.

I conclude by telling my youngest son, Rich, that since he's just beginning junior high school, he'll be in a whole new dimension of life's responsibilities. I say how proud I am of him already, and expect he'll deserve that pride in the future.

4/5/14

Wandering around grounds of an abandoned insane asylum or 19th century hospital. An area like an empty neighborhood of separate, decrepit buildings on a little grid of streets. Through the almost floor-to ceiling windows I can see inside rooms where peeling paint and puckering plaster are like a "skin disease of solid surface.". I see sinks and claw-foot tubs, their exposed piping severed and mangled.

Driving my pickup truck through a salt marsh with a lot standing water. But I don't slow down even at one place where it's deep enough that I feel splashing through the firewall, and the engine become erratic. But I make it to an elevation of the dirt road I'm on, come to a dead-end beside a dumpster behind a strip mall, back out, drive up over an embankment onto a lawn. Beside me now is a church and before me is a well-paved road onto which I turn.

Inside some building where there are a lot of other men, young and older. One of them seems to be my Uncle Bill [who died many years ago for whom I worked summers in his business]. There's an antique piano in the room and with his encouragement I sit at it and, in the dream, seem to be concertedly and intricately directing each finger to the key it's playing. But he's disappeared and I go to another room where Ron [dispatcher at the trucking company I retired from last year] is saying something to me to the effect that I must be becoming upset that I'm so old and don't have that long left to live. I tell him it doesn't bother me.

It seems I'm outside the same building and noticed that I'm not focusing well. There's a heavyset girl with thick glasses nearby.. I suddenly have her glasses on and see very clearly. I return her glasses, put mine back on. I tell her I'll have to get a new prescription, although now I'm seeing clearly through my own lenses.

In the VW beetle with me are a driver and a bunch of dogs as fellow-passengers. But then they're all evicted and,, like Eskimo sled dogs, running ahead of the car. But this is so they can, like hunting dogs, flush out game for us. But then it's as if I'm up above and ahead of the racing retinue – and I'm looking down when suddenly blizzard conditions appear and on the fenders and hood of the still speeding VW all the dogs are clinging to each other, huddled, a big canine pile.

Parked beside an inner city intersection filled with cars. From a huge truck I'm supposed to make a delivery, but in order to get to the freight I have to temporarily just let other things drop to the street, such as cardboard boxes and numerous clumps of broccoli. Traffic's stopped at a red light. I hear a woman's voice from a car and she's saying that I should be given a ticket for excessive littering. But then between her car and my truck a guy in a pickup with vastly oversize tires squeezes, almost, and stopping at the light which is now atop the edge of a loading dock in front of the stopped vehicles and my truck. The height of the dock is less than half the diameter of the guy's front tires. I watch, fascinated, as the light turns green and, like an insect surmounting a rock, the pickup truck tires seem to vertically roll up and over the edge, of the platform.

[I awoke for a few minutes, but went back to sleep. During the couple more somnolent hours, it was as if I was "rehearsing" these dream segments so that I'd remember them to write them up. But churning in my dream-mind were also several other matters with which I'd be concerned when I finally got up for the day.]

4/7/14

Riding a bicycle, my wife, Angie, comes racing down the corridor, which is also a street. On one side there's a cemetery behind a fence. Angie been in a heated argument with some town committee, and to cleanse our souls, it seems, we find ourselves naked in a plastic, modular tub and shower unit. The water sprays insufficiently and cold. The unit is tilted significantly.

Angie announces she's not getting out until there's and agreement made on workers' rights. I take the responsibility to present her mandate to the committee, Despite her determination to stay in the shower, she's with me as I look for my winter boots under a cluttered rummage-sale table. I can't go into the council chamber unless I'm wearing footwear. I find the boots, put them on, noticing that they're on the wrong feet.

4/8/14

A couple streets over there's oceanfront. With someone else I've entered the first floor of a gutted building Apparently some interior rebuilding is going on. Someone skulks around outside, peers in, sees me. A cop soon enters where I am, determines that I'm just looking, and suggests I should leave.

Outside I'm in a parking lot [very much resembling one by a beach in Marblehead, MA]. A cop has pulled over my grandson for speeding in the Oldsmobile that my father had owned fifty four years ago. A stern warning is issued, but no ticket.

Now, just outside the gutted building and that cop gone, I'm with someone in a car and rather than just leave the area, I want to turn down a street where it's evident that all the houses are vacant, most of them with plywood over doorways and first floor windows. In the dream I sense that I'm seeing Oliver Street in Malden, Ma, but also I'm experiencing a "flash-back" of several long-ago dreams where I'd either be driving through or in a couple cases flying over vast sections of slums and tenements all deserted and desecrated.

There seems to be a party or neighborhood gathering and it seems to be in my house, although the rooms and furniture aren't familiar. Ron, a neighbor when lived in Franklin, appears and it soon becomes evident that he's become a Born Again Christian. We go into a room where he sits on chair and I kind of sprawl on a mattress.

As if some length of discussion had already taken place, I'm telling him that I'm glad he's "gotten religion", but that I have reservations about literalism and fundamentalism – but that I won't get into details with him unless he's interested. As if fast-forwarded, we've come to discuss the Bible as God's unquestionable word, giving Genesis as an example and what happened in the Garden when Satan tempted appeared and tempted Eve.

I interrupt, Nothing is said about Satan, The Bible says it's a serpent.

Ron protests that there has to be interpretation according to the worshipper's understanding.

A reply that literalism cannot allow interpretation. I present an example: "Thou shalt not kill. If those are God's words, then by what right would any worshipper assume that a particular situation or person (war or prejudice, for example), would provide an exemption from the command. Given individual interpretation, anyone could come up with his "mortal" justification for killing, interpolating that the Commandment doesn't cover his particular case.

Ron paraphrases a related, but contesting, statement by "one of the earliest Evangelists – famous guy . . . ."

I tell Ron that in the last year I read through the whole Bible, Old and New [which I actually did] and wrote and published four books.

He's amazed, asks where he can see a copy.

I tell him they're down cellar in my writing area. Suddenly I remember the evangelist, Billy Graham. And the last part of the first segment of another night's dream consists of my continuing with Oral Roberts, Jimmy Swaggert, Jim and Tammuy Baker, Jim Jones, Father Divine, Joseph Smith, Dwight Moody, Billy Sunday, Jerry Falwell . . . . . and it seems I list more but the dream has faded to impression only.

4/9/14

Inside a restaurant, but it's a bank too and a young woman is telling me that it's no wonder the doors were locked (she'd let me in after-hours) because of the big bounced check. I notice her long, stringy, underarm hair.

Driving on the shoulder beside a highway. Seems to have been a railroad, the tracks gone, but gravel and cinder surface obvious. Suddenly I have to swerve because, rising out of the ground at first mangled, is chain link fencing. I continue to find myself with an unknown passenger. A major intersection of two-lane highways is empty of other cars. Crossing and proceeding uphill all at once there's deep snow and I shift into four-wheel-drive.

The snowed-in highway dead-ends in a seaside lot full of boats in various conditions, from well-kept and –covered in plastic . . . . to decrepit and interspersed many that very much resemble torsos in various states of decay and dissection.

4/10/14

[The previous day I read half a book about the design, construction, and operation of the Athens, Ohio Insane Asylum. It was one of those massive, Kirkbride-design buildings, four story central section with tower, "wings" stretching and kind of "zig-zagging" out to each side. The book told of the 18 million brick used, timber framing, embellishments such as wrought iron grating and woodwork, etc. When operational, such things as inadequate storage areas were mentioned. Also, that some rail-line was installed to facilitate delivery of people and provisions to the place. Anyone interested in the fascinating (and sometimes horrifying) history of mental

health in America should search "Historic Mental Institutions" or similar-worded sites on the WEB].

Re. the above, my dream. At first I seem to be in either a warehouse or a freight car. There's freight-sized door beside me, and the floor level I'm on is several feet above the ground outside. Around me inside are some other people, unseen, and all of us are somewhat "immersed" in indistinct objects such as boxes, perhaps pieces of furniture – but the only distinct content which is my concern, and apparently to be responsibility (for now it seems I have something to do with the construction of the Asylum) . . . is a bundle of 4" x 4" timbers. Though overall about 16' long, a few stick out more than others. I notice that those few have been carved or milled as if they're to be used decoratively.

[The previous night I'd watched a PBS program about animal prosthetics. One was a two-wheeled cart-like device on which the rear portion of a pig would be strapped (the pig's rear legs were non-functional), allowing it to propel itself at running speed with its front legs, and its body just roll along. Other creatures shown: horse and dogs with prosthetic legs, swan with prosthetic beak, even an alligator with a tail prosthesis (its having been bitten off by another alligator)!]]

Dream flash: some kind of creature dashes from one side of my "mind's screen" to the other . It seemed like the entire animal was on wheels. And that was that.

Another extremely brief dream-event seemed to combine the asylum book and a second PBS program I watched last night. The program concerned animal intelligence, especially crows, ravens, jays. One experimental layout consisted of cages arranged side-by-side in a row.
In the dream, I picture a long institutional corridor with innumerable office doors opening off it. But without seeing anyone or hearing anything, I realize that an order has been given to all the professional and clerical occupants of those chambers that they're going to have to shift their places "down one cage" from their present space.

I'm next in a vast back lot behind decrepit buildings. There's junk around on the potholed and fragmented remains of paving. I'm to take a trailer-truckload of freight to Presque Isle, Maine. But I suddenly realize that I should have inspected the condition of the rig before. It's almost dark and after noting that some of the marker lights on the rear of the trailer don't work, to my greater consternation I see exposed wires, one actually severed. As I'm about to pull out of the lot, a massive German Shepherd jumps onto the running board and tries to get in. Truly his is a "barko-profundo". I'm thankful the window is shut.
Next, I've tried to pull the rig (now shrunken and like a "little red wagon") through a Walmart-like discount store and into its back room. I'm not going to be able to get it through the narrow space between the counters and rear wall.
And I'm back in the back lot, realizing that I have to return to the trucking company terminal to have the wiring repaired before I can embark on the Maine trip.

    I head back by way of a street close to where I lived as a kid, then making a turn (of necessity partially over a sidewalk) off onto a street obviously four towns away (in reality).

    I'm upstairs in a tenement building, it seems. My mother and father are ready to embark on some trip, all packed. I'm relieved that they'll be gone, so not worried about my trip, about which they know nothing.

    On toward the trucking terminal. And then I'm there, park out back in an alley, pick my way between junked tractors and crunched trailers and other massive debris. I enter the sagging garage building, find someone, and tell them the situation with the wiring and necessity for immediate repair so I can get going to Maine.

    For a moment I'm talking with the dispatcher, who's inquiring if I'll be able to give him another day's work when I've returned from Maine. It seems I've already officially retired.

    I return out back. The rig's gone from where I left it. Repaired, it's in an adjacent lot full of damaged cars. As I make my "walk-around" safety inspection of the rig, a speedboat and the trailer it's on (nothing towing it) comes speeding toward me, I can see a couple playboy-types in it.

    It tips toward me . . . .

    I realize I should wake up and write all this down.

    I don't until an unknown length of time later.

4/11/14

    Driving along a winding dirt road. On an embankment above me are all kinds of junked heavy equipment including bulldozers and WW II era tanks. The dirt road crosses a bridge under which passes a wide, former railroad line (tracks gone), and as I note the endless straight stretch of gravel to each side I consider it would make a great trucking bypass route.

    I've arrived at some city, manage to park the rig, and set out to inquire about the location I'm to deliver to.

    It seems that, rather than acquire directions, I've spent an interim meeting the woman from the foodservice company who brings the "meals on wheel" that I deliver to various elderly individuals [actually] a couple days a week. I back my pickup truck to the rear of her box truck. She passes me a big bag and as soon as I take it, at least a gallon of some kind of juice pours out. We decide I should just leave the bag leaning against the foundation of the building beside us.

    Back at my parked rig I find my dispatcher [from years ago] waiting for me. He's concerned about the condition of the truck. We jack up the front axle and discover that the front bearings are so bad that one can kind of flip the wheels back and forth [which was the case with the truck I first owned]. Dispatcher tells me that the terminal manager has ordered that I deliver the load and immediately get the rig off the road for repairs. I reply that I've already booked off for the afternoon since I have an appointment. [after delivering meals on wheels today I do have an appointment].

    In a warehouse. A pallet of boxes of various canned goods has sort of collapsed on the floor and the manager of the place is stacking the strew so it can be two-wheeled into my truck for my return trip. It seems that I've delivered my load there.

In a long corridor [very much resembling description of the interior of an insane asylum in a book I'm reading – but also corridors in a hotel in movies]. I'm trying to find my daughter's unit. I'm at a door that's opened and asking the woman within where ………'s unit is. The woman replies, "She's a jerk." I hold up my hand to silence her from further insult, informing her that she should learn some tact and at least determine with whom she's speaking before deprecating anyone.

On down the corridor, turn left, through a set of double swinging doors. I arrive a a large vestibule occupied by a group of people, many of them small children of various ages [PBS program recently pictured interactions of little children]. A couple just beyond toddler age approach me. The little girl is trying to tell me a spittly secret. The little boy is fascinated with my left arm which has suddenly become extremely sunburned.

4/12/14

In a cluttered tenement apartment that I'm renovating, actually restoring to some kind of grandeur. My late wife is tormenting me, accusing me of ruining her life and forcing her to live in a dump. I'm angry, then anguished, then almost breaking down, I dash out onto an upper level back porch enclosed by storm windows. She's out there after me, and I escape, emotionally agonized.

On the ground, down over a stone wall. There, a commercial vehicle is parked and I climb in. The interior of the cab is in ruins, wires straggling, upholstery torn. I look out the window and on the potholed pavement a bit away I see two figures. They could either be penguins, one large and the other small, or commas of different sizes.

4/13;14

A warehouse, entrance off an uphill alley. It had been occupied by a dealer in fancy parts of demolished buildings. But on my arrival it's now empty except for some tables and a number of elderly women in fancy dresses. I'm told that the demo dealer will be back in an hour or so, but for the interim the ladies' organization has rented the space from him.

Rather than wait, I decide to proceed to some other destination of importance. But as I'm departing a woman in a car comes the other way at an intersection and from the perpendicular street (at the intersection) a young African rams into the side of the woman's car and the two cars seem to pirouette around a couple times before coming to a stop. I see no damage or injury so drive on.

I back out onto a parkway. A speeding car swerves, tires smoking, to avoid me.

I pull off the parkway onto a curving street with two-decker tenements on each side, all of them gutted but to be rehabbed. Their facades are right against the sidewalks which are right against the street. At the edge of the street all along, metal poles have already been installed so that the sidewalks can be fenced-in from the street. It seems a good safety measure, but resembles the "chute" through which cattle might be driven from their conveyance to a slaughter-house.[I just finished reading a book on the meat industry and its profits to investors but overall loss to the communities in which the facilities are located).

I'm running from room to room and bed to bed and some commando is chasing me and frequently punching me until my face is a mess. I emerge into an area of the fraternity house I lived in and a the young men gathered there tease me because the other guy "got the best of me".

I'm my adult daughter in a two-seater little device like flying saucer. We're racing along a suddenly there's a massive jolt that throws us out and renders the vehicle inoperative. It's my responsibility to repair it. First I'm able to reinstall the upper cam shaft push-rods that had been dislodged. The saucer is now as small as a Rhumba (robotic vacuum cleaner). After studying the thing I realize that to reinstall the bottom push-rods I'll have to tip it over and undo a central screw so that the top and bottom can be separated and I'll have access to the innards. Doing so, soon I'm looking at an intricacy of machinery (in the dream) as realistic and detailed as if a picture in a technical magazine,.

Finally young guys and I are walking up the slope of a field behind an arc of the back porches of tenement buildings [an image of the actual area where Huntington Ave. and South Huntington meet in Boston]. One of the others is wondering what he can get for a joke-present to give to his girlfriend. I tell him about something I read about somewhere – the guy's gift to his girl was Testosterone. I'm questioned what would be the result. I reply that I don't know, but it might be interesting. The final words on the matter from one of the others was . . . . . that whatever resulted, she'd still have a vagina.

4/14/14

I've just had surgery without anesthesia, so I'm only able to crawl up the slope of a huge hill. I'm dragging what looks like a big punching bag, but it must have some clothing and other provisions in it.

High above, I'm looking for my aunt's house, but I suddenly realize that she died a dozen years before and the house is someone else's now. For a mere flash, I'm in a tenement apartment where Aunt marj and some other old women are seated at a table and she's not angry that I haven't been in touch with her for awhile. I realize that in another dream I'd been in the same room.

Outside, a massive customized Buick limousine passes me as I turn down an alley which becomes like a sluice, partially blocked by debris, and a channel for water. I let the bag I've been dragging plummet down ahead of me. It's momentarily stopped on a sand bank, but I free it and move on down.

Into an area that could be the bay of a heavy equipment repair facility – very high ceiling. The place has something do a men's exercise club. I help two elderly guys lower down and fold up a canvas curtain that had served as the outside door. But there's still about a six foot masonry wall separating the interior from the exterior. I've climbed atop, and as I pass various objects to load onto a vehicle outside, there's some rather manically euphoric lyrics being sung on the radio . . . ."coming from our gain in Maine and we're heading to New York City where it's always pretty, and we and baby will see things free . . . . . "

Next, loading things into the back of a station wagon: shovels, planks, the bag I'd been dragging, branches shrubs, and trash.

Resembles Maine St, Malden, MA, close to where I lived for a couple years up thru 4th grade or so. I'm my adult age in the dream, apparently wanting to visit a doctor's office (could be because of the unanesthetised surgery). The door's locked. I stand on the sidewalk, wondering whether to wait and notice that my smart phone, as if it were a piece of ceramic tile, has a large piece of a corner chipped off. But my concern is interrupted as I recognize (from years ago) a miniature collie dog. It remembers me, runs to me, jumps up and down, and then almost grovels and smears itself on the ground, overwhelmed with dogdom happiness. I try the doctor's door again, the dog suddenly morphing into a house fly on the door which just as instantly takes off down the street while turning back into the dog.

As I walk away, a young woman passes and at first I think she's the doctor's receptionist. But as we chat for a second I find out she works for the dentist further up the street.

My late wife Angie and I are at the bottom of a sloping field. We've parked there because it seems we can't drive over the rutted and soggy path to reach the AT&T phone store that's high up on the hill. We're suddenly inside the store. I show the salesman my damaged phone. He's the one who had sold it to me, and seems most eager to resolve my problem – which is to get a replacement of the same model But then it's a young woman and a different guy presenting me with a tiny, basic flip-phone;. I persist that I want an exact replacement. And the next model I'm shown is about the size of travel bag, and to access the keyboard a glass panel has to be unlocked and flipped up. Also, I'm told I'll have to pay for it sine AT&T doesn't warrantee for chips.

Realizing the phone would have to be carried like an attaché case, I turn to tell the salespeople that I don't want it. But only the girl is visible and she's running up a ladder to get away from me. I chase her, catch up at the door to an inner office area, and insist on a smart-phone exact-model replacement. She seems contrite, promises she'll have one for me in just a moment, and she enters the door. I decide to follow her just as she drops through an opening (like a trapdoor without its door) in the floor.. Back outside, down the ladder, I demand to see the store manager.,

4/15/14

I'm driving a tractor-trailer rig. Pull into a curved drive, through a gate, and into the yard of an industrial building. The office tells me to continue on to the warehouse in back. They tell me they'll unload me out on the main street. I should go out there and wait. It'll be awhile.

As I drive out toward the main street, I notice that I'm heading toward the place again, even though I'm also approaching the Main street. Where railroad tracks cross the street I'm on, I see a woman pushing a baby carriage, a couple young children walking with her, and a huge horse bending its head down and nibbling at something in the carriage.

Out on the street. In the dream I realize that I'm in Lynn, Ma, But I'm also on Broadway, in Somerville, MA, from one moment to the next the slope of the wide street changes from downward one way to the opposite.

I stop, a cop tells me I need to pull up. I proceed too and have to get back close to the intersection of the street from the horse and this main street. That's where my truck will be unloaded. Taking a chance I back up half a block. Wait a long while, and for some reason decide to leave and come back later.

I find myself with my niece Jane and another adult woman. We're sitting at a long table on which there's an electronic keyboard and for some time I'm playing around on it, producing some admirable music. But, thinking of the delivery I'm to make, I have to get some sleep.

There's a brief dream-discontinuity in which I've just walked at least five miles down the long and steep hill to the trucking terminal. One of the young drivers starts to rib me about staying in shape at my age, and I inform him of my walk, and that I do at least 2 ½ miles a day. He looks impressed.

But I'm suddenly back where I'd been and just awakened from my nap. I ask the time. It's 4:25. Horrified, I realize the place may be closed before I get back for the delivery unless they run a night shift. I have to call them. Ask for a phone. Jane's friend brings me out a short stick with a wire attached,. I fish in my pocket and find a tiny flip-phone on which I'll try to call my dispatcher to get the number of the delivery location so I can call them. I keep punching a wrong key on the phone which repeatedly displays ":this number call cannot be completed".

Suddenly it occurs to me that my smart phone with the large number pad screen is in my pocket. I go outside to be sure of a good signal. I start to punch make the call.

4/19/14

Looking out the window I see an upscale regions of rolling landscape, largely open fields, but upon which are very expensive old home homes, surrounded by the acreage. The closest dwelling I like a oversized cottage, many gables and oriel windows and such.

I've just had a psychotherapeutic session and the therapist leaves.. A woman in the room with me, who seems to be a psychiatrist (perhaps she subcontracts sessions rather than conducts them herself). She says, "What a nice man that man is,"

I agree and tell the woman my observation about the guy. I figure he must live in the area. That he would be nobility in a different age and country than America. I ssk her if the man could possible be the owner of the nearby home.

She tells me she wasn't talking about the therapist, rather, that I should look out another window. That perspective is out on what looks like a city intersection. Several strange looking creatures, human-but-not, have bunched up at the corner to wait for traffic to clear so than can cross the street. I see clearly that one of them is a blue-faced Bozo (as in McDonald's clown).

Still with her in the room, I'm facing a set of bookshelves, one of which is about desk level. It seems something about my session has required me to take a test on that shelf. I'm being somewhat facetious when I ask the woman if it wouldn't be a good idea to fasten another board to the shelf so that it's twice as deep – like an actual desk top. And I continue that the next session I'd thus have room for my dictionary. She thinks it's a great idea. I tell her I was kidding, for I figured having my dictionary at a session would be cheating.

Still in the room she's been talking about being Jewish and having grown up in Israel. As she's about to leave I say that I consider Israel to be part of this country, part of the U. S. Her first response is that she thinks it preferable that Israel be independent. But then she considers that being part of the U. S. would be greater security and save lots of Israeli soldiers' lives.

After she's departed, I find that there's been some kind of combination vcrafts fair and business meeting in the room I'm in. For some reason the floor has several large sheets of plate glass on it, and around and on them are piles of computer printouts and broken artists' paint brushes and just stress. It's my responsibility to clean the place up and I carefully pick up the sheets of glass. One's perimeter is almost fractal. Another, thicker and nicely rectangular, I make sure I don't step on.

In a car with someone who seems to be one of my adult sons, but also a friend from back in high school days. We've just come into downtown Melrose on Main Street. On each side are stores, some with upper floors, others one-story. Every one of them is boarded up. In this dream I realize that in a previous dream only a few were. In front of some the proprietors are slouched or seated.

My companion and I are walking now, and turn to step up into one of the stores. Across the street someone waves at us, perhaps recognizing me from when I'd lived in Melrose 55 years before.

4/20/14

I've purchased materials from a building supply company. The locale where I'm to install a wide door appears to be an immense, empty exhibition hall. I've carried in the door frame pieces. But I realize I haven't brought the actual door with me. I lean the frame pieces against a wall, take a measurement to make sure I'll get the right size, head back, and seem to have procured the door and about to leave the building supply yard.

A sudden shift of scene as I run up a flight of stairs and push open the door to what had been my bedroom in my house in Franklin. The occupant of the room is quite surprised at my sudden entry. Realizing that I no longer live in the room and it's rented to him, I apologize, complement him on his décor and furnishings, and realize I have to live immediately to install a door.

Before I depart, he and I consider his idea for a window that overlooks (apparently) a street in Somerville, MA. It's typical height off the floor, but the wall it penetrates seems to be about two feet thick and of stone. The guy's idea is to enlarge the opening down to the floor to have access to a balcony or deck he'd have built along the outside of the wall.

My response, as we depart the room, is that he himself will have to go to the City of Boston building department with some kind of drawing, consult with them on the legality, and then pursue hiring a licensed contractor to do the work which he would pay for.

I'm outside and can't find my tape measure or keys. Then I'm inside another cavernous space where door frame pieces are on the floor but I can't measure them. And I realize I have to because when I took them from the building supply yard I left the door behind.

Outside again and extending steeply downhill appears to be the arcade (long main corridor) of a two-level shopping mall. Rather than shops and stores, houses and larger structures including exhibition halls are alongside the wide walkway. I'm on one side of the upper level, separated from the other side by a kind of linear atrium which extends from the lower floor up above where the skylights are black because it must be night. [picture the interior of a two-level mall that's sloping downhill).

[As I dreamt I realized the imagic-duality of mall interior and Route 2 from Belmont steeply down toward Fresh Pond Parkway in Cambridge]

I start running, Faster as I gain momentum downhill. There are college-age people here and there, more the further I go, until I reach a point where a cluster of kids step in front of me and stop me. I protest that I have to get the door I've left behind.

One of my sons apparently in his early twenties seems to be with me and advising me regarding how to manage my life without my tape measure and keys and what to do about a rolled-up rag I'm carrying. But he's gone when I reach a ;leveling and widening of the "mall-ish" avenue. The resemblance here is a typical mall food court, but somehow fused with a parking lot which, however, is full of church pews, some of them totally enclosed as in colonial protestant churches. Of the crowd of people, most seem to be immigrants. I sit on one end of long bench-pew. At the other is a heavy-set Hispanic woman and her children.

I deeply ponder whether I'll be able to get to where the door is before the place closes. But I consider it would be petty, yet presumptuous, to pray.

[A couple days ago my son (now in his 50s) and I took a long "mall-walk",

Albeit in a one-story mall. But during my career delivering freight, I was very frequently in multi-level malls, and also on route 2 going into or coming out of Cambridge. That section of route 2 was an open cut, an excavation, in which the six lanes of the highway were bordered by high concrete walls. Atop the walls on each side, at what had been the original height, were streets, somewhat like access roads, but fronted by houses and a store here or there. I hope these words convey the image similarities of shopping mall and route 2. The food court image is "mall-derived", of course, but at the "foot" of route 2 in Cambridge there's broad traffic circle, quite configurally similar to the round space of the food court.

I spent yesterday with my daughter and her husband, a very dedicated born-again Christian. He and I talked in some depth for a couple hours, exchanging beliefs based on vastly different existential contexts. Not an argument, it was an exchange of ideas, his almost solely Scriptural, mine inclusive of Bible (which I read completely during the last couple months), but recognizing that, to me, recitation is missing the point of what existence represents. . . . and missing the points where the Bible is not only conflictory, but outright contradictory.

Of course neither of us was converted, I to be born again, or he to be to worship God as the super-ordinal of and in all things.]

4/21/14

I'm driving just the "cab" or "tractor" part of a tractor-trailer rig. Going uphill and beside the road and below, there's swampland with little streams flowing through the debris of dead fallen trees. Even without pulling trailer, the upgrade is such that I can't get up speed and there's a line of cars behind me. But I have to bet into Boston. Images of the main road through industrial areas of Boston suburbs flash momentarily,.

For some reason I've decided to head in the opposite direction. But now I'm on foot and there's snow on the ground. I've suddenly come to a semblance of Andover, about 30 miles north of Boston. Through the snow I trudge off the highway and into the rear of an empty parking lot, its restaurant closed. Beside me in a little building, some kind of equipment is running, probably heating the restaurant.

Now concerned because of the snow and passing time and that I'm far away from Boston, I cross a vast intersection (resembling part of Lowell, MA), and on a side street with old two-story brick buildings on both sides, their first floors occupied by stores with dirty (or boarded-over) plate glass windows. I decide to hitchhike.

I'm picked up by a middle-aged woman who has come out of a frame two-decker with a young boy amid others, some young girls of various ages, who are upset at being told they can't go with the woman and boy. But this instant-intrusion in the continuum of the dream was only image-flash. For I'm in the car with the woman and boy and we're driving along, the brick buildings on both sides. I have a book, and the woman comments that it must be on some kind of "man's sports". I reply that the only things I read are "long-hair", complex, like cosmology and evolution and religion, and I average a book a week. She's impressed, says she wouldn't have time. I tell her "you have to utilize every second. Even at a red light I'll pick up a book and have time to read a paragraph."

The boy, perhaps 12 seems friendly but says nothing. I'm told that the woman is taking him (her nephew) to see her son who, because of some learning disability, has been living in some Midwest facility,.

We continue and the rather major urban street just ends, a narrow lane the continuation steeply downhill. Several detail cops are directing traffic many workmen in hard hats are involved in various site work including taking down overhead branches from trees and parts of electric power grid stanchions,. Inching along, we finally reach a parkway onto which we'll merge. It resembles the Fresh Pond parkway in Cambridge (which was involved in last night's dream).

In the trailer park where I live, I walk along between the streets. Someone unseen, is advising me that I can profit from listing the various "inflatable technological devices" I've fabricated in the book I'm writing. That way people will have a choice of where to live as they move into the park.

4/22/14

My Grandson Nick is with me. He's a teenager in this dream. We're looking at a road map to determine the best way to get to where I have to go. Route 17 out of Somerville, MA arcs up around the North American continent and leads to where I soon find myself driving alone. The scenery is Lakes Region New Hampshire's valleys and hills and distant mountains.

But then I'm in a small city, somewhat Maine seacoast-ish, it seems. A supermarket has just opened and the crowds waiting to get in are out in the parking lot. Having no hope of purchasing anything there, I lean against a cement block wall and realize that I can't find the phone number for my niece, Janine. The purpose of my trip seems to have been to visit her and her family. And next I can't find my phone. Or car.

To get somewhere, perhaps to find the missing, I walk through a hallway with a counter on one side and large windows on the other. Perhaps due to stress, I pass wind – very odoriferous. Passing teenagers glare at me and then make humorously deprecating remarks about the old man.

A restaurant interior is my arrival. At the table next to mine a pair of elderly, rather elegant, women are discussing the genteel ambience of the establishment, its excellent food, and admirable décor. On the table in front of me is a cardboard carton, at least 18" in each dimension. I've opened the top. I'm peeling back the plastic that sealed the simmering contents, and I'm just about to feast on "boxed beef bour-gui-gnon".

4/23/14

A small city. Downhill, the street comes into a wide intersection. Seems like Portland, Maine but with no visual resemblance as I drive, my meticulous, managerial son my passenger. I ask if we should go on up to Weld [the tiny Maine town way up in the mountainous region where my other son and I used to go camping every year – not my passenger]. We agree it's too far. We don't have time.

A brief consideration, as if a contemplation: How fine a man Jackie Robinson was and how he broke the color barrier in Basketball!! [my passenger son's name actually is Jack and Jack is an absolute sports fanatic. Robinson was baseball, of course]

Suddenly downhill more and we're driving in a sort of alley with tall, decrepit industrial buildings on each side. The brick walls are obviously saturated from years of being exposed to machine-oil and fumes. As we pass some of the openings of various sizes, I see that inside there are piles in places, mounds, here and there one of the interior bays stuffed from floor to ceiling undifferentiable debris and equipment. On the ground at one place is a gigantic, antique chain hoist somewhat resembling a huge insect whose intestines (the chains) are straggled out from its body.

To my passenger I comment, "This is my kind of place."

4/24/15

Many feet below the broad expanse of deck (or dock) the sea is placid. The view out over the water is very Medterranean. The dwelling from which the deck (or dock) extends is opulent and the home of a man who had started his out penniless and built some enterprise having to do with the ocean into an empire of wealth,.

[I've recently read a book about shipping magnates (Maersk, Onassis) and others] and the Exxon yearly statement with pictures of docks and ocean expanses]

The man had more or less adopted a young boy some years before. Now in his late teenage. The boy and the man's beautiful daughter have long been in love and afraid that her father will forbid their marrying, they elope. But soon they're back, for some reason their plans defeated.

The young man climbs up onto the deck. The father, enraged, rushes toward him.

"Give up those guns," he *[silently]*shouts/ "Is said get rid of the guns."

"I have no guns, There are no guns," the young man protests.

The man grabs him, they s scuffle and struggle to the edge of the dock. There, the man is in control, almost dangling the young man over the edge of the platform, from which a fall even into the water might be lethal.

Scene shift to young man at a narrow door as if to the rear stairway of a tenement, but approaching him calmly over the deck is the father,.

"I love her. She loves me, We've done no wrong. We want your blessing," the boy cries in utter anguish, his face distorted in grief-frimace.

"There are eight others for her hand before you," the father states.

Inside the dwelling, it seems. Have I become the boy? But there's nothing more about the father or the girl, Rather, through a broad, office-building-like corridor I proceed toward an opulently furnished dining room *[images from books and DVDs]* where I'm soon standing on a chair and stepping over onto a buffet. I'm trying to replace curtain rods on brackets *[as I'd actually done in my own dwelling the afternoon of this dream (though not standing on furniture to do it)]*.

Unseen, but known to be the insane aunt of the beautiful girl, a woman's quavering voice *[though unheard in the dream]* conveys a continuum of complaint and profanity. The salesman of a company I worked for decades ago is sitting on one of the dining room chairs so I can't step from the buffet onto another chair. But seeing him I realize it's getting late and I'll be late getting to work.

But it immediately occurs to me that I'm no longer driving a truck, so my new position allows a flexibility of when I arrive and leave the job, as long as my responsibilities are taken care of.

The complaints of the loony accompany me as I walk past various doors off the corridor,

4/27/14

The view is down upon an industrial spread containing somewhat ruined buildings amid clusters of pipes and storage tanks. Amid this, here and there, are apparent areas of disposal. In the dream I recognize the vague resemblance of the elevated roadway and what's below to New York City's Pulaski Skyway. I had not been on it for almost 60 years.

A former business partner is with me in the cab of the tractor-trailer I'm driving. *[said partner's wife and I just made contact on LinkIn after 35+ years – the dream truck image was the truck I actually drove for a brief period when I worked for my relatives' building supply company.]* My passenger and I seem to be in our early twenties.

We come to a dirt road which steeply descends to where a construction project is taking place. The building's several floors are like steps set onto and into the slope. We park on an upper level and go inside, looking for a masonry contractor amid the open framing and strewn floor. After some time someone is located and discussion ensues as to who's responsible for unloading the trailer. The load is bricks, all had loaded in rows from front to back, no pallets, no packaging. Thus all will have to be hand unloaded using a special "brick clamp" that lifts ten at a time.

The contractor very grudgingly agreed to unload the trailer. I toured around the site *[noting as I dreamt distinct similarities to two sites I'd actually delivered to in my driving career – as if their images were intermixed]*.

After some indeterminate period of time I seem to have awakened from a nap. I make my way across the construction site, over a trench,, around the corner of the building where workers are removing panels that seem to be cloaked in mold.

I'm next with my late wife, thus having aged forty years from the construction site, We're in a Chevy dealership. The floor slopes steeply down from us. A salesman has quoted me a price on a "Spark" {a subcompact hatchback.) I offer $500 less and he looks at me with disgust. No deal, so outside I'm picking my way across a field strewn with junked auto parts and boulders.

Back at the construction site. The trailer is empty. I'm suddenly in a panic. How long has it been empty How long did I sleep? I'm going to be very late getting back to the building supply company. Where is my partner?

As if peering through a hole in the upper wall of a movie projection booth, I'm next seeing a flickering projector's light, a man behind it holding a book and a microphone. He's reading something by Hemingway as narration for whatever is showing on the unseen screen. Another man off to one side seems to be contributing the voice of another of the book's characters. Between the fluctuating light and wafts of fumes and smoke, a fleeting association occurred to me -- of this scenario and Orson Wells's invasion of the earth radio program.

Inside an abandoned, totally empty building. Perhaps 40 feet wide. Ceiling almost unseen so high above,. Length behind me stretching back to a vanishing point. Ahead of me I can see a way out. And I must reach it, for the place is filling with smoke, smoke coming from the distance toward me as if flowing liquid. The rough walls and floors around me seem like concrete ledge, cavernish, the place utterly empty.

I must hurry to where I now discern a commercial roll-up door and wonder if I'll be able to find the switch make it open.

4/28/14

On a narrow, two-lane highway at first through a flat area with fields on both sides. It's like the old route 1 in Topsfield where the fair is held each year. There's heavy traffic as I start up the steep hill. A massive truck with many axles comes roaring down going the other way. Ahead of me there's a small cluster of vehicles stopped as two pickup trucks try to turn into a dirt road at the same time.

With a woman first outside a building where reconstruction work on the façade is being done. Various pieces of masonry and trim have deteriorated and some already fallen off *[info from book I'm reading about NY City buildings]*. Several stories up large blocks of stone have been removed from a wall. I express my admiration for anyone who'd work at that height with the weight that each stone replaced must weigh. At another place on the façade wall, I count the number of tiers of brick. Inside, within a labyrinth of structure and people milling around, I manage to find the interior of the column I'd counted outside The number of tiers match.

A park. In a car with a fat woman. We've watched a gang of kids tear loose a water cooler and tip it on its *side [image cooler torn loose from "One Flew Over The*

Cuckoos' Nest?]. She tells me her husband does the same thing. He lays the bottom part on its side and fills the water jug itself with jet fuel. The he lights it and the thing goes off like a bastard.

I mention how dangerous that is.

She says how disturbed her husband is. But therapy hasn't helped.

I offer that perhaps he's so insecure that his only sexual prowess is by his getting a water cooler off. And if so, she should give him all the love and support and sex she can.

A broad expanse of grass stretching both ways across the street. On the other side a one story building with a porch the extent of its long façade. A low bed trailer, similar to an open U-Haul, is backed up to the porch. My late wife, Angie, and others and I are loading things from inside the building onto the trailer, But *[ex-neighbor when I lived in Franklin]* has already prevented our escape once. Now we're trying again. Moving things out of the building, Repositioning things that had already been on the trailer. One is a big hydraulic jack. Another, a metal chest with massive hasps. Inside the building there's a confusion of things, some within storage bays that divide one wall. From one of the bays Angie wants me to take a slide projector. I tell her we don't have time to watch family slides. If Ron comes through the gate onto the grass across the street he'll cross the street and stop us again. I pass her a battered suitcase to load on the trailer. She peeks into it and sees it's full of old paint brushes. Aghast, she almost throws it back at me. I ask if the brushes are pubic hair symbols to her.

The trailer is almost loaded. I'll cover the various objects and boxes and with a piece of rubber roofing *[such as covers the mobile home I now live in]*.

Ron hasn't appeared. But across the street, passing the gate from the park-like lawn to Ron's yard, a woman is walking a dog without its being on a leash.

4/29/14

The place seems to be a parking lot fused with a boat storage yard. I drive up a ramp from the couple acre hollow and just before turning onto broad avenue pull over to the side to make a phone call. A woman already parked there looks at me with disgust.

I'm supposed to go through Malden, MA. And suddenly I'm in the center of Malden where my father (unseen) comes up to me at a stop and tells me that there's a leak and a ventilator motor malfunction at 848 *[a building I owned years ago on Huntington Ave., in Boston]*. I tell him I haven't owned *the* place for years, but decide to check out what the situation is. Now on a bike, I go up Malden's narrow Pleasant Street. On the left there's a crowd of people, mostly elderly women, around the entrance to the building of concern. I make my way through them to the entrance. None of the beautiful brick work I'd done remains, the front part of the first floor gutted and even floor removed so that I m looking down into the basement. There seems to be laundry and dry cleaning equipment in the gutted realm.

> *[Years ago in Boston I gutted what had been an elegant mansion, even removing partitions between the huge rooms. The place being converted into a nightclub. Years since a residence, the lower floor, still embellished with intricate moldings and coffered ceiling and all, had been used as a*

dry cleaning business, obsolete and defunct washing and pressing and steam generating devices filled the floor space.]

I depart, depressed. On up Pleasant Street I ride the bike. I've decided I'll take the road that winds around the Stoneham reservoir. At the top of the Fellsway it occurs to me that trucks are now excluded. I ponder how I'll proceed from where I am to where I have to go which is really back the other side of where I've come from.

Reaching what might have been a school building but now was municipal space, I ride the bike up a wide staircase with age-worn treads. Next I'm in a large room, now sparsely furnished office. Two women have expected me and what I'm to take from there to someone somewhere has been nicely packaged in high-end store's shopping bag.

[Just above, truck exclusion, reservoir, Fellsway and more are "shards" of places from my personal past. The buildings involve "grafted-on" images from a book I'm reading (and websites surveyed). If any of this dream content is Freudian or Jungian or otherone's then I sure have odd erotic cathexes]

4/30/14

A crater or an open pit mine. But there had been a neighborhood of three floor tenement homes, of which only a couple, kicked-out, porches falling, are still even structures. Around them and off here and there are crumpled remains of the demolition of others.

The ground is drastically rutted and crevassed and hardened up into pinnacles and elongated hillocks above knee-high. The substance, solid now, must have been the composition of saturated clay, or even at one time submerged. Perhaps heavy equipment had caused such drastic deformations.

A small crowd of people are gathered. There have been deaths, it seems.*[this image from an article about the recent Ferry capsize in Korea. But the grieving woman had been my next door neighbor in the trailer park where I live]*. A tiny Asian woman is the focus of concern, especially mine, as she tells of disappearance of her son. It's unknown if he's dead or alive. And her husband has gone off, leaving her alone and unconsoled. He has trespassed through yards and even into houses searching and all feel he is psychotic with grief. But the poor little woman has no one even to hold her. I experience an impulse to. But I don't, realizing it might be at least inappropriate in her culture.

On a long stairway descending into cluttered oblivion. I sense I'm in one of the remaining buildings in the crater-realm. To one side there are extremely long windows, almost like "glazed slits", one of which I'm removing and carefully tlting so I can lower it to the floor below and let it lean against the wall. Suddenly outside in a garage building the window I'm holding has become a small, rectangular unit with a section of stained glass centered between a mosaic of leaded clear panes.

In a car. Leaving that area, Uphill and the land is more a surface, like an immense, mars-scape dimension parking lot. I head for the gigantic dumpster, pull up beside it and stop. My late wife is upset that I'm going to scavenge, but one of my grandsons (teenaged in the dream) explains that it's necessary.

For in a sort of duct space beside the engine that may run the dumpster's compaction equipment, the object has been left for me. And it's strategic, crucial, that I obtain it.

I exist the car, lie on the sooted ground, Wriggle my way into the space. Can't see. Grasp something, As I pull it out it tips and a little and gasoline pours out. I reach back in and, yes, I have grasped that dire necessity that gets quickly put in the vehicle so we can leave the drastic domain.

5/1/14

I'm considering that eating their rotted flesh is held to be the highest for of revering one's family members who have died. But this might pose a problem for one who is volunteering at a hospital.

In order to get where I'm going I have to pass through a street where several trucks and a few men are involved in poles and wiring. One of the poles looks new. Another is leaning over so far as to threaten toppling. And the third supports a web of wires. For a moment the men delay their operations to let me pass.

As if wormholes through some fabric between universes are the tiny spaces in the towering hedge through which I crawl at first. But realizing this difficulty, I'm next just climbing over the top and about to drop down on the other side. Several coins fall out of my pocket onto the ground below. I pick them up, noting that there was once a tennis court where I am – perhaps part of a long-gone estate compound.

At my almost-100-year-old aunt's house which now has a wall of green plastic panels. Each panel is like a deep-relief scene of something military or religious, and the configuration of these rectangles similar to a great cathedral door in Venice. But these are plastic, and the green seems to be mold and I begin cleaning one of the panels until I realize I have to be at the hospital to volunteer.

The enterprise seems to have just moved onto the property. The last truckload of junk and debris is being driven down the slope which suddenly is sloped in the opposite direction after the truck has left. The young guy with whom I'm soon talking is the proprietor, or son of, and he's sympathetic at the commuting I've been doing. It seems I'd tentatively arranged to stay at my aunt's house. But this place, with the several acre sloping lot and single-story building, is apparently either where I'll be working or right next to it. It's agreed that I can put a small camping trailer over at the edge of the property and live there whenever I want to.

The young man and I go into the building, down a ramp, and in the empty basement level I see suddenly a page of print which I realize is from a combined auto racing and anthropology magazine. It's concerned with the advisability of handling and eating carrion, even in honor of the dead – and having anything to do with the living in a hospital.

I must call my aunt to let her know I'll not be staying. I must see what time it is.
   [This will be my first day volunteering at the local hospital. I'll have to awake much sooner than usual, so the concern for the time. As for the rest of the dream content – bits and pieces from various sources: reading of the Rockefeller who apparently was killed and eaten cannibals in New Guinea – that famous Cathedral door – the distance I used to commute – my aunt – initial request to put a trailer in the lot of where I worked –

recent Comcast pole workers in the neighborhoods . . . . .etc. etc. etc.]

5/2/14

Big house on a hill. Filled with people. I'm leaving with my 90+ year old aunt and as we proceed down the steep, slippery walk, I'm realizing something about nails that were hand cut, not machine-made and my father (dead for years) advises me that I should visit my aunt for I haven't seen her recently.

The next location is the vacated and somewhat desecrated remains of what had been a mansion. More recently a flophouse *[a building in the town where I live that's being renovated]*. And old high school friend and I are between the structure and the railroad tracks in the rubbish-strewn lot. At first I've wanted nothing to do with the place. But suddenly I'm intent on renovating it. But my friend says he has to get some sleep. I tell him I'll start and he can join in later.

I walk past the "cease and desist" sign that the building inspector had posted beside the door. Someone had previously been doing unlicensed work *[such sign posted on a unit in the park where I live]*. I'm inside. Through somewhat of a labyrinthine corridor, up a back staircase. I begin pulling newspaper that had been used as wallpaper and/or insulation from off the back wall.

But then I'm outside the place. Way in back where a brick and concrete addition contains industrial activity *[once including manufacturing WWII submarine parts – this imagery from Hudson, MA where I used to pick up freight]*. I look around for the way in. I hear voices. Around a corner I see a staircase which leads to a platform and a freight door. At the expandable grate that blocks the entry I get someone's attention. Inside on a lower level I see trucks being loaded.

I'm asked whether I want to be a driver or a guard. Considering that I don't want a full-time position I say "guard". I hear whispered discussion concerning how old I am.

While I stand there I notice to my right, on the upper level, there is a row of perhaps six forklifts moving a few feet forward and then backward as if they were some kind of shuttles in a machine. One of them is mouth-operated by a quadric-plegic and by puffing or sucking on the little tube she can make the machine go forward or backward, stopping critically at points where on the floor there are little metallic contact buttons. At each of these stops a sort of stylus automatically drops down from the machine and creates a brief circuit with the contact on the floor.

Back outside, walking toward the decrepit mansion part of the complex. I'm having second thoughts about getting involved in restoration. There's too much for one person to undertake. It wouldn't just be a matter of paint and repair. Perhaps the entire electrical would have to be redone.

In the narrow lot between the façade and the railroad tracks I conclude that I'd better make an appointment with the building inspector and let his expertise (and municipal "rule") be the determinant of whether I should get involved.

5/3/14

Upstairs. A room long unopened. Inside, a tall steam radiator (hot) tips over and becomes a long electric radiator. I find trace the cord into a hole in the wall and unplug it. No wonder the electric bills have been high.

In an alcove above there are numerous small kitchen appliances, one of them a waffle iron. I have no idea why they'd be in a bedroom

With my wife, Angie, I begin carrying various things out of the room into a hallway. Mattresses will go into the attic.

Outside in the backyard of the same house I'm taking objects to the driveway for removal or disposal. A section of fence falls down. A shed collapses. The yard is suddenly exposed, vast, with various strange shrubs or cactus-like plants as well as trees growing.

Inside a cafeteria where there's a nightclub atmosphere and rowdy crowd. Outside the plate glass window a bunch of bikers pull up, dressed somewhat ivy league. They and those inside the place are shouting back and forth until one of them manages to convey the information that someone's wife or girlfriend is in the hospital.

Where I next find myself, in a bathroom, naked except for some kind of medical fixture on me that almost seems like erotic bondage. I'm giving a urine sample, but can't stop peeing. The cup is full, and I'm still full and I dump part of it into a sink while letting my overflow go into the toilet. But I've dumped too much out of the cup so pee more into it but again it's too full and I am no longer peeing.

It seems like a good idea that I dress and conceal what ever the equipment is that's binding me and creating almost unbearable erotic sensation.

5/4/14

Walking along the top of a stone wall. On my right is ground level. On the left is a 20 foot drop to a lower lawn. I'm looking at the lower roof-level of a church. I'm supposed to be in it for some kind of service. I'm in it. But I'm told I'll have to wait for the religious ceremony because those who will conduct it first have jury duty.

I'm driving along and see, above me, a vast flock of wild turkeys. Some are flying very low, irratically, almost "wagging" their bodies in the sky.

Having arrived with some kind of fabric that unraveling from a roll, I enter a tenement-like house. But the location is in the middle of a field with not another structure to be seen. A pleasant young woman has opened the door. As she and I climb the stairs something's conveyed about the residents being lesbians. I'm concerned if they'll like the cloth. Three heavy-set, older women are eating at a table. None looks up. None speaks. On the wall behind one is a gigantic spider. She notices it, grabs it, and begins pulling its legs off before hurling the wriggling remains out the window behind her.

5/5/14

Walking along a road that seems to be beside a harbor, but no details are seen. My cell phone rings. It's the wife of my old fraternity brother. She tells me there's to be an African drumming festival at the park and wonders if I can join her and Howie. I'm about to say I will. They live just beyond the Cape Cod Canal, about an hour's drive for me. I ask where it'll be specifically. She tells me Baltimore.

My phone goes dead.

Later it's recharged and I call. She tells me she was putting me on. And so we talk a moment about a load of weathered (barn siding) wood I'm supposed to pick up. That, she tells me, is in Cincinnati.

In a VW beetle, having done something to the carburetor so that the engine finally runs smoothly. Howie and I have just left his house, walking down an extendable set of stairs that I assume can be moved from house to house for real estate sales purposes. We have to get to Malden. But I should go to Medford first. In Medford in a school corridor with office off each side but the students won't tell me who I should see.

So back in the VW and it's decided I'll meet Howie on the way to Malden where I have to pick up some kind of hardware that will have something to do with the load of wood in Cincinnati. A fleeting glimpse of Exchange Street in Malden fades.

I'm on the cell phone as I drive. Howie's wife is telling me that he's sitting on their new white chair eating cheese puffs and that he's said "for what it's worth I'll shed my intestines."

5/6/14

Around me is a vast expanse of concrete surface, cracked, sections somewhat tilted, truncated protrusions of what must have been concrete walls of the ,many buildings of a WW II era industrial park or military installation.

Horizon-distant I see great clouds of dust billowing into the sky, reminding me of "dust-bowl" documentary pictures I've watched on TV. But I'm able to discern that several machines are causing creating the dust here. As if enlarged (or my eyes have binocular-vision momentarily) these devices are like dune buggies with huge, rotating, round brushes (like street-sweeper machines) at the very front.

Two twentyish, rather derelict-looking guys approach me. They're friendly, so my initial alarm is alleviated. Each has a device which can best be described as a combination of a golf cart to which a clear glass vat is attached. Atop the vat, which has various tubes and coils seen within the liquid it contains), there seems to be the upper part of a vacuum cleaner. I ask. They tell me.

On a previous occasion, they'd been thrown out of the stadium where they'd gone to watch a professional game. The reason? Drinking. And so they'd created these devices to contain a sufficiency of beer for whatever length the game they were now going to would last. And who would throw them out because of "liquid-handling equipment"?

They go off into the distance. I survey again the desolation, now giving the impression of a long-abandoned commercial airport after some devastating seismic cracking and crazing and tilting of its surface.

Next to me there's suddenly a wall. Cobblestones set in cement. About 6 feet high. The top is capped with brick. About four feet from it, on my other side is another wall. And as I step out from between, I see that there's a series of these walls, as if they were built to provide "bins" between them for gravel or mulch stockpiling. The brick capping and first couple tiers of one wall is partially dislodged. I push on it, let it spring back, push harder, and after a few reciprocations the whole top mass falls to the ground.

5/8/14

The crowded restaurant is a city center and from a corridor people entering are also traffic-flow into the congestion circling a round table which is also a vehicular "round-about" (or traffic circle). The people are upset, for they have to provide information to some director of the chaos. He is marking on a chart the information he's given regarding who will be chosen to be taken off somewhere. I comment that it truly could seem like the end of the order of the civilized world. A response is that prior to technology this would not have taken place.

Somewhere, for some reason, an audience is being instructed that when they snip off the ends of wires, those with yellow plastic coating are to go in one bowl – those with white in another. And then it seems these same people are in a line streaming from a railroad yard. From among them at least two young women have been selected to perform. One of them is hiding within the crowd as an agent or promoter tries off to one side tries to lure her out. He's a meek little man with a too-small suit, and he kind of bobs his head as he entices her to not be so shy,.

I realize that within the load of scrap earthmoving equipment tires deportees could be trapped. Several people could pull apart the closure of the rubber, and force the person in. There would be no way for the one thus enclosed to be able to escape and his journey with the scrap load would be his slow death from starvation and thirst.

But an auditorium and a stage and all then is black except the eight or so musicians illuminated and they perform rock while members of the audience discuss how degenerated music has become. But I find a way to comment on the excellent classical orchestrations and performances (especially by the London Symphony) of rock music by The Airplane, Pink Floyd, Beetles, and many others. On the stage the ensemble become airborne, at first just hovering as they play, but then almost like a octet-mini-swarm circling and angling intersecting trajectories until they finally become as a single "linear" which cavorts and contorts in all sorts of configurations as if a "performance of concert-calligraphy".

The downstairs little lunch room is empty except for the other cop, a woman, and me. She's to be married but goes into the kitchen area. I, in plain clothes, experience a vague heartbreak. But up the tiny staircase I knock on an apartment door. The shift of illumination through a viewing hole precedes a voice asking who it is. I respond that I'm just checking that everything's alright.

5/10/14

` Driving with other in the car. Uphill through a decent residential neighborhood, two-story single-family homes on each side. We come to where the street levels off and there, some young man has committed some kind of crime and is escaping out the Restaurant hallway. Out the front door I start to run after him, but he's disappeared behind the house next door. I return inside, flip open a little battery-holder-like thing on the gun in order to be sure it isn't loaded. On the porch several people are involved in crating some kind of equipment or machinery and packing personal belongings for the escapee and someone who will accompany him to take on their trip to Portland, ME.

Back in the car. Now, from the house, a chubby adolescent girl squeezes into the back seat. I make sure I can shut the door without squishing any part of her. We proceed, now downhill. Residential thins and soon it's open land with weather-worn and warped barns here and there and farmhouses off the road at a distance. I'm wondering if I'll come to a dead-end in someone's field.

But it's the parking lot and paved rear area of a very large church in which I avoid various obstacles, equipment, vehicles that are haphazardly strewn on the rough pavement. Have I dead-ended at a church? Which is symbolic of my death coming soon? And the little girl is my next incarnation? In the dream these ideations flit.

Suddenly, still in the car with its occupants, on a wide city street very suggestive of Washington St. in Roxbuty, MA in front of the Post Office building – but also of Moody St. in Waltham. I put on my directionals to make a left turn onto a side street. An cruiser driven by a woman cop is coming in the opposite direction. She starts to accelerate and just as I slow to let her proceed ahead of my turn, she abruptly slows. Assuming she's being courteous to an old man, I've just begun to pull ahead of her when she steps on it and I have to actually swerve drastically to keep from being hit.

There was no accident. The side street is a wide street ahead of me. I know not where it leads.

5/11/14

There has been a contest of a cappella singing groups. One of them was my entry and my son was in the ensemble. The audience reaction was obviously that my singers were the best. But the judges gave first prize to another group and one of them, a dignified Negro man, glares at me, enjoying my disappointment. He then dislodges his false teeth so that they're grotesquely protruding from between his lips.

In one small assembly hall Biden is being interviewed about solar energy. He's not doing well with his responses, even using a double negative. I'm in a sort of foyer off that room, and off the other way is a similar hall where Boehner and another top Republican politician are actually mimicking and mocking Biden like a couple adolescent boys.

I'm holding two sets of electrical cords each of which consists of two lengths. I could unplug the sets and re-plug them each to the other. But I realize that one is the main power for my stereo system and the other has something to do with automotives so I'd better just leave them plugged as they are.

Wondering which of my three vacuum cleaners I should use under the bookshelves in the living room.

5/12/14

Silvi McInnernny's dually pickup truck has the long hay trailer attached to it. The rig is idling at the corner of one of the streets that dead-ends down among the towering old brick buildings. Once the Boot Textile Mill, the structures are being converted, after years of abandonment and decay, into housing.

The intersection has become a corridor and across which an elderly woman walks and looks at me. I'm on the other side of the intersection, the perpendicular street having become a stairwell steeply down and then just back up to where the woman is.

I'm in a small room where there's a huge concert grand piano on which I'm playing with such dexterity the arpeggios and classical segments and rhythmic and tonal counterpoints that I'm amazed and wonder where this ability is coming from. The woman has moved on from her moment of listening.

But my father appears and makes a devastatingly disparaging remark about my playing being the mere performance of a poseur. Though my father, his appearance is the redneck drunk who lived next door to me [in actuality, in Franklin]. Distraught, I've exited the two-story building and am standing on the snowbank between it, and the next door building's driveway. As I wonder how I'll survive, how I'll pay my cost of living, an Asian exits the building and throws several cigarettes into the snow.

Within some building. At a table. I'm telling my father how what he said hurt me.

And then I'm in some proximity to Harvard Square, back among apartment buildings. One of my sons in his thirties is there, and we're suddenly outside and in back of the building where there's excavation and construction going on. He indicates a heavy-duty rock or metal cutting machine on wheels and comments on how deafeningly loud it is and how annoying that the college kids insist on pushing the "surge" button that makes it even louder when cutting especially tough material.

I've argued with someone and departed from the building through vague, misty imagery of parts of Ipswich, MA salt marshes and other seaside proximities. But then I've decided to walk from somewhere (Ipswich?) to Harvard Square. But I don't have my cell phone with me. So how will my son and his family know that I'm walking.

And it suddenly occurs to me that the distance would take at least a couple days to traverse on foot. Yet far enough along, it's too late to turn back.

Then that son, another (this one maybe 12 or so) and some other people have brought me off the street into a building where we're discussing renovations.

5/14/14

Driving.
A realm of intersecting streets going up steep hills and long ridges with old two and three family houses close together but with little yards and drive-way space between them.

Turn at an intersection and the street dead-ends. Retracing, there's no street to turn on where I'd turned off a street onto the one which now dead-ends at its other extreme.

Turn at an intersection but it's a driveway into a backyard that drops off almost precipitously in the valley below and between the hills and more houses off into the distance.

I'm lost in that rectangular reticulum, and have to find my way out so I can get to work. Or is it so I can find my way home from work. I don't know. I can't tell. I'd departed on this trip on my bike. Now in the big old Oldsmobile I inherited from my aunt, I'm driving.

Lost.

A city. I'm driving. It's night.

I'm in a stairwell in a commercial building where there are numerous landings but no exists from the stairs. But then I'm driving, the Olds having shrunk, in a corridor in the same building, it seems. But there are no doors off the corridor and the corridor comes to a dead end.

Outside again and back behind a semi-demolished metal building, perhaps once a rounded-top (Quonset) type of structure, but now crumpled, angular, and with a yard behind it filled with junk. Some begrimed mean are siphoning some fluid out of a five gallon glass jug and joking about drinking it and the enhancing sexual effects it might produce.

Still night. The same city area. A dead end street, more like a wide alley back between buildings. I need to find my bike. It may be in the loading dock area that's like a cavern into one of the buildings. I park the car. Enter cavernous receiving space where Oriental women are sorting various objects on a table.

No bike.

I need to find it so I can, it seems, get home. For now I want to call my wife to tell her that I'm lost and it'll be awhile before I join her. But I realize I have absolutely no money. "Not even a quarter for phone call!!" I shout to the women sorting the freight.

Out on the street.

The car's gone.

I ask a women passing by, but she knows nothing of its removal or, now, location. Around the corner I ask a parking lot attendant and he suggests that it was probably towed for illegal parking.

I have no money to even make a phone call to even find out if it was towed and, if so, where. And even if I had, I had no money to pay to get the car from where it had been towed and pay whatever fines and fees would be involved. And I don't even have a quarter to make a phone call to tell my wife that I won't be home for quite awhile, for even if I found my bike, I'd have to ride miles along the Interstate highway and now it had begun to snow. And it also occurs to me that I have to get in touch with my dispatcher to let him know that I won't be able to get the freight I've picked up back to the terminal for awhile.

Disconsolate, I begin walking along an avenue where land on one side is first forested, but then drops down and ramshackle, clapboarded buildings with huge windows covered by thick screen abut the pavement. On the other side there's a broad expanse of park. At a major intersection, a street through the park goes off, a perpendicular from the one I'm on. A couple women school-crossing guards are lecturing a cluster of little girls about the sin of singing some song using the lyrics they've been using.

I'm on the street through park. It comes to a campus-like expanse with various brick buildings.

In one's reception area, I'm told that I can have an immediate appointment with one of the junior executives. Into an office I'm led. At his desk, a thirty-ish aged, immaculately dressed, dignified but very cordial and friendly, African man. We sit and I've explained fully, it seems, the above predicament I' in. And he's acknowledged that he'd be able to resolve all for me as far as occupation and opportunity and necessary logistics, including phone calls. . . . .

. . . . except that his employment has been terminated. And he continues with his sad story of not knowing how he and his family (three kids) will live and where they'll go. "I'm Allen. And you [he looks at his appointment calendar] you're Ap Schneider."

I tell him about the people who bought the absolute wreck of a trailer across from mine in the park where I live – how the guy totally gutted and then redesigned and rebuilt the whole interior. I respond to his amazed question, "He did everything himself.
"Including utilities, Ap?"
"Gas, electric, all to code. He's skilled in everything you can imagine. But," I continue, they're selling the place and moving to Tennessee. Maybe that's where you and your family should go. He bought a big, brick house on a couple acres, barn, carport, massive cellar, beautiful interior. Low hundreds."
"Yeah, we'll have to look where property values are lower than up here."
I've left his office, the building, the campus, the street through the park, and now I'm going off into some unknown distance until I can find a way to get in touch with my wife before too long. For she must miss me. The dispatcher at my trucking job should realize that I've been retired for almost exactly a year now and not expect me back.

5/17/14
They've moved out across the street. Seem to have been very degenerate people who've left a mess all around the yard and almost destroyed the house.
On the other side my son's ex-mother-in-law seems to reside, or be staying. I'm involved in some kind of renovation of the first floor rooms: the kitchen, and a large living room. The work is intricately interpretive and I'm worried about getting it done without going beyond the contract date.
But I have to leave. Brenda (the ex-mother-in-law) has yelled out the window and I've awakened from a nap. I tell her I'm tired and have a chest cold, but will continue the job tomorrow.
Driving as a passenger in a truck. The operator is an old high school friend with whom I established an e-mail correspondence a couple years ago. From the front to the vehicle something is protruding off to one side and we're worried we'll spear a pedestrian or parked car. A wheel threatens to fall off. We've reached a destination and are about to head back as I wonder where to hang a long-handled hoe so it won't fall off.
Back at Brenda's I'm walking through the cellar to leave. Tools are strewn all over the place, but I'm too tired to organize. As I leave, I'm being told that the people who'd moved out across the street were on the news. One of their daughters had been found to be a princess and heir to an immense fortune.
I comment that instead of broadcasting it, a guardian attorney should have been appointed first and her inheritance secured in trust.

5/18/14
Again I'm driving, now on a hilltop road. To the side the land slopes down steeply and there's no guard rail. But when I come to a car stopped ahead of me, I swerve between it and the drop-off to get by.
Then in another vehicle. This one is being driven by Mort Silin. Silin was a financier and money-lender with whom I had a second mortgage years ago – a man of the upper echelon, at least in economic measure. He's taking my wife and me for a visit at his home as if we were intimates or even family.

Before we arrive at his house, he detours up a dirt road that dead-ends in what looks to have once been a quarry. At a sort of vertex, hundreds of feet down from the surrounding tops of the cliffs is perhaps an acre of flat land. Otherwise we're at the bottom of almost a cylinder except for the narrow aperture where the road had entered.

We arrive at a very modest house set apart from others, surrounded by overgrown underbrush. And suddenly I find myself alone outside, going to take a walk into the nearby town.

There, at first the appearance is that of any small city's main street with stores on both sides. But I next find myself behind the stores in a sort of service road or alley. But the passage is cluttered with damaged or obsolete dry cleaning and other commercial laundry equipment, crates and boxes, and numerous people and the over-all effect is that of an equipment dump and a busy oriental bazaar. For the people seem to be shopping.

And some of the boxes and crates are being unpacked by, apparently, employees of a supermarket. I manage to get by all this clutter and activity and find myself back on the main street, but with no idea how to get to Silin's house.

Walking behind other' houses, through yards, opening gates, I've entered a VW bug and am driving on a road going steeply uphill. It suddenly plunges downhill and I just manage to stop before I'd have plummeted over the edge of the cliff right in front of me. At the bottom is the "vortex" area where Silin had driven us.

I try to back up but the wheels are skidding. I reach out the window and push on a tree, but that doesn't help. A couple other people pushing and I manage to back up to where I'm safe and can turn around. But first I look down in awe of the now-conic chasm below, where water swirls around the ledges and churns at the bottom.

5/20/14

The Romans have departed otherwise, leaving only Al Pacino, seated in one of those battery-run invalid chairs that disabled people use in the super markets. So high above the actual ceiling of the vast, cathedral-like building (or is it steel fabrication mill?) we're in is obscured by an overcast of smoke and soot and dimness.

Al's relating telling me and the others (unknown) with me about his experiences in the construction business, especially how he hated doing plumbing back when sewer pipes were cast iron and joints had to be fitted by pounding oakum into the cracks between the pieces prior to molten lead being poured in. So much easier now with plastic pipes and "radiator-hose-type" clamps to hold them together. And he continues to tell of his brother, who died, somehow resulting from construction work.

"He had it inscribed on his headstone," Al says. "A whole list of instructions for his workers so that it wouldn't be necessary for him to still be alive to get the job done right.

Through streets of houses, single-family, a feeling that it's not far from the ocean those these are more substantial than cottages. Turn right onto another street and then back through overgrowth and rubble on both sides as the road narrows. Turn right again and it's between dunes until suddenly into an industrial lot.

On one side is a freight dock. Scrap metal is being thrown down from it into a 50 gallon steel drum. On the far side, the lot is separated from an elevated rail line over which a lengthy freight train is passing. The cars are both flatbed and gondola type, and both seem to be overloaded with various unidentifiable metal, equipment, devices, all mashed and mangled.

I've climbed up on the dock and find myself inside the warehouse building which is the trucking terminal out of which I [actually before retiring] worked. But its interior now is split-level, the higher part almost like a balcony. On that upper level a couple my former co-workers greet me and wonder what I'm doing back. We discuss whether I should consider working part time – but only driving on short-run very local deliveries or pickups.

Back out in the lot below the dock, the drum is full of scrap and I'm to wheel it on a hand-truck to the other side of the lot which, thankfully, slopes downward toward the rail line. And the rail line is no longer elevated, rather, it's in a sort of open-topped tunnel.

At the end of the lot I almost trip, and the barrel tips off the hand-truck. Some of the pieces of metal fall below beside the tracks. The manager [who was my former terminal manager] of the place comes down, not angry, but anxious that I climb down and somehow pass up the pieces to him. There are no trains scheduled for some time, so I feel safe and the pieces aren't that heavy.

In a ballroom- (or even exhibition hall) sized space I'm moving long, ceramic pieces of crown ceiling molding and leaning them against a wall. A woman apparently supervising the construction work is next with me as I show her work that I've been doing in my residence: intricate brick paths and wall mosaics and antique barn beams – all, it seems, in a state of incompletion and disconnection. She doesn't seem impressed and I'm depressed that I haven't accomplished anything in my years of artistic-architectural effort.

It seems to be on the other side of the railroad tracks from where I'd spilled the metal. It's a residential street. My former neighbor, Marie, lives on the first floor in one of the two-family houses that line the street. Two of my kids, eight or nine or so, seem to live there. They're down the street aways, and Marie calls them to come and say goodbye to me, for I'll be leaving with her. But first I have to go to the bathroom.

The bathroom seems to be a single molded unit, shower, sink, toilet, all one continuum of contoured, white plastic. The doorway is arched, the door retracted into a slot. It takes me awhile to find the button to push to make the door automatically emerge from its hiding place.

5/21/14

Having to get out of bed fast because my father is coming to go to sleep in it and I realize that the alarm clock has been ringing for at least an hour and I've just now wakened. Naked, I dash out over the second floor porch of a three decker tenement building and find myself in a field where I watch a dog running at top speed toward the steep embankment beyond. Attached to is small utility trailer and he struggles up the incline, but quickly reaching the top at which point the trailer has turned into another dog. A length of chain leash extends between the two, and the first dog turns his head and bites onto the chain, and with a swift swivel manages to pull the second dog up and over the lip onto the road above.

5/22/14

In a field on high ground. In a sports-utility vehicle, one of several there as if there'd been some kind of gathering. But then just me and my adult son Richard in the one vehicle and we're hurtling downhill on a dirt road at the bottom of which there's no way to proceed other than by going up and over a stone wall. But having done so, we're within an enclosure of stone walls. I caution that he may tear out the bottom of his vehicle, but he proceeds up and over and . . .

. . . . we're now in the same vehicle but it's become amphibian and we're cruising along a seacoast lined with fine homes , probably once cottages. The area looks much like Marblehead. At one of the homes we drive out of the water up a ramp and park in the yard.

Several women of various ages are carrying pieces of metal, some of which resemble bed parts or roof trusses, with difficulty getting them out of the building and onto the broad porch that faces the sea. Evidently all these were pieces of some elaborate intrusion protection that they'd had installed, but had found to be worthless to prevent entry. That there'd been a rape in the neighborhood recently was the reason for their wanting to be protected.

One of the women, perhaps in her seventies, reminded me of Estelle Getty (Maud's mother on Golden Girls) in her silent sarcasms to the others. But there was no physical resemblance.

I seem to have been responsible for some extensive restoration work in the house, and have left the job unfinished for a long time, though no one seems upset. They're too busy passing metal out the front windows.

Next, I've walked back into the building to consider what I still have to do to complete the job. Through one large room that I'd completed some time before, I realize that I'm re-experiencing the image from a dream of almost overwhelming, incomplete contracting work several years ago. A dream-image remembered in the imagery of a dream!!!

But in last night's dream, most everything is complete except for a kind of extension from the main building. This contains a bathroom which almost seems encrusted with intricate wood trim, but otherwise almost in a state of ruin. Above the gouged and rotted remains of the parquet flooring an old claw foot bathtub and a toilet with overhead tank are attached to exposed plumbing and tilted. Above them, the walls soar at least 30 feet upward to a sagging ceiling.

To (my son-image now fused with an ex-partner when I was doing construction?) someone with me I confirm that, yes, this area is part of what the job requires and it's been ages and I haven't touched it.

And I realize that I drastically underpriced the job.

And I further realize that I don't have any working capital.

And I wonder if I can get away with just painting everything, hi-liting the details of woodwork and even pipes.

And I realize it was a mistake for me to get into this line of work.

5/27/14

Behind the house the bare, dirt yard slopes downward toward an oblivion. Looking the other way, I see the building, a one-story high sort of elongated bungalow with a porch that stretches all the way along the front – which faces the back where the yard slopes down.

I have in my hand a quart can of blue (color unseen but known) paint with which I'm to paint the whole expanse of the porch including numerous columns and innumerable balusters between the top and bottom rails between the columns.

Suddenly in the basement of the place where a long corridor is partially flooded and I walk over various pieces of floating debris from a large room where a party seems to be going on. But I'm alone, heading away from the others into the desecrated darkness of a beyond into which the corridor leads and as I try to stay upright as the floating footings shift, I realize I should never have gotten into the renovation business because I don't have enough paint even for the façade.,

5/28/14

Waiting in the reception room of a mansion [image from Fifth Ave. Mansions website] that is now a nursing home. I'm to drive a resident to a medical appointment but he hasn't come down from his room for some time though attendants have told him there's no time to spare.

A middle aged black couple are there, having waited far longer than I have. But they seem almost ecstatic, despite their delay. They lock their arms and pivot around one way, then the other arms and pivot the other direction, as if engaged in a square dance. I'm so moved by their euphoria that I reach out to the man to shake his hand. On his brown skin his five o'clock shadow is absolute black. I tell him how he and his wife would be an inspiration for anyone who is impatient with anything.

I've next come down from the hill in Melrose, having already passed the house where my old high school friend (and still communicant) Alex lives. But it seems to be some years ago temporally fused with the present, for I'm to have dinner with his mother who died some years ago. I turn onto Lebanon Street heading toward Malden and when I realize that there used to be a cemetery on the right, but now there's just a swampy wasteland, I know I have to turn around and go back.

As I retrace the mile or so, at one point a very distorted horse, some kind of pouch hanging down from its belly, is trotting on the sidewalk toward Malden. I come to the intersection where I'd turned onto Lebanon Street and it's turned into a hallway in some apartment complex where two women are talking.

One is telling of her missionary work in the Orient where young girls are being abducted and sold into sex-slavery. The woman's organization has been successful in saving many girls, but not curtailing the business. The other woman asks something about male children. The reply is that girls are the only concern because a boy is just a man in formative state (and I assume that she's assuming that the brutality and atrocity of the sex-slave trader dwells already in the male psyche of any age.)

But I say nothing other than to express my respect for her faith and its efforts to provide fulfillment for people's lives. As I continue, stressing that to me Christianity is such doing, not praying and preaching, the other woman's face takes on an almost transported appearance, as if enraptured.

But the hallway has dimensionally warped into an office of a trucking company where I may (or not) have brought in a load, or be supposed to take out a load. Others in the room are known to be there but not seen, and I depart out into the warehouse area where pastries and candies have been served amid the piles of freight and debris of damage and pallets and pieces of equipment. I spot a large bag of jelly beans, but by the time I've skirted around to the other side of a crate, they're gone. All that remain are some "orange slices", partially flattened somehow. But I take them in the remnants of their bag,

Walking down the ramp to the lot below, I realize that I need to get the trailer from inside the warehouse. I'll be pulling it with a motor scooter that I've already started, but can't find a place on to put the orange slices.

Walking back up the ramp, I'm considering that I should not have gotten into the commercial transportation business without better equipment.

5/30/14

Kenny and I are about to embark on a bike trip up into Maine. He's in his twenties in this dream, thus I'd be in my forties. He was the son of my next door neighbor in Franklin. His wife, Michelle, is quite upset because it's very cold in Mass, thus will be much colder up in Maine.

Through desolate, empty, high ground we pass for some time. At the summit of this region there's the remains of one of those massive historic resort hotels (like the Mount Washington or Balsams) which we see only the back side of,. We then come down onto a highway where I ask directions. We come to a small Maine city and turn off the street to descend into a service area behind commercial buildings. Up a twisted set of iron steps we're on a receiving dock. Then we find ourselves in a restaurant's kitchen.

Several culinary employees are there and one of the things I'm discussing with them the route we'll take to go on toward the New Hampshire border – and whether massive ruins of the industrial building [featured u several past dreams] is still there. I'm told that the place was the Pease Factory.

Down into the lower lot. As we wheel our bicycles up to the street I notice that it's almost freezing already. And then I see a very thin dog sitting up straight almost right beside me, It turns into an oboe for a second, then back to a dog which is soon running alongside me as I ride my bike. The dog's and my heads are cheek to cheek and we're kind of kissing sideways, sharing a solution of saliva as if a communion of species.

5/31/14

I'm in Andover, Mass, north of the center. It's a neighborhood of old homes on large lots. But the houses seem to be three-family. And the one where I am is the site of an auto repair business run by some young Hispanic guys. My VW bug is in the driveway and they've already done $400 worth of some kind of work on it. I'm advised to leave it another day so the can finish. I express my concern that I'm paying $400 a day to have the oil changed.

I have to get to my volunteer job picking orders at the local hospital stock room. The young guy in charge indicates that I can borrow the old sedan he's backed out, so I take a big cooler and some other things out of my car and put them in it. But I have no keys, so go up three flights of winding stairs in the house to find him.

He's not there, but I find that I'm naked except for a towel which I wrap around me. When I'm back out on the driveway, a bunch of little kids and a couple women are in the car and I can't get my possessions out of it. Several of the mechanics are leaving the property in a big dune-buggy-like thing but tell me they have no idea where the boss is.

So I'll have to run to get to my volunteer job. But I'll be late.

Though naked, I seem to have a pocket in which there's my smart phone. But I don't have the number to call the hospital to tell them I'll be late. So I start running. Out of the neighborhood. Out onto the main street which goes up a long, long hill to reach Andover Center.

Along the way, for a moment, I'm in a sort of sunken auditorium around two sides of which a narrow sort of catwalk is the only access to two narrow sets of stairs down to the main floor. Empty now, someone with me is informing me that this is a school and the whole setup is definitely against the building and safety codes, for the room will be filled with hundreds of students with no other escape in case of emergency than the two narrow sets of stairs.

But I'm back on Mass Avenue, naked, running up the hill, noticing a bicycle go by with two front wheels.

I've reached the center of Andover, gone through the crowded lobby of a ritzy department store where elderly people are gathered. I emerge again onto the sidewalk and notice that at ground level two buildings are far enough apart to walk between, but up ten feet they touch – and I wonder if one has tipped. But then I notice the protrusion of a massive granite lintel block which cantilevered beyond the lower wall, thus the buildings continue upward "conjoined".

On the other side of the street I'm crawling over a couple spaces where the sidewalk paving is missing and the spaces are strewn with bones. Ahead, I see a truck crane partially blocking the street. At that point I'm in the building into which a single fork from the boom of the crane is being withdrawn from a little slot in the masonry, and as the boom lifts, it seems that the whole of reality around it is descending. But I realize it's just relative perception illusion.

I've reached a destination. Not the hospital stock room.

It seems to be some kind of chapel perhaps in a monastery. There's a rough, plank table, on both sides of which men are seated. At the head of the table seems to be some official or even sacred personage. One of the men stands and proceeds to rant and rave about his wife who's an "extremist Protestant" who refused to join him in worship of a scientific-religious fusion savior because (he holds up an icon with Albert's image engraved) . . .because Einstein was a Jew.

Naked, amazed, I watch a little door open to reveal a little slot and a little lever-like arm extend quite quickly and, like a cue stick to a cue ball, poke the protesting guy right out the opening to drop down out of sight.

[The diversity of imagery in the above derives from all sorts of sources of experience in my life – places delivered freight to in Andover, Hispanic car repairs run out of once-elite neighborhoods, etc. The hospital volunteer job is my actual ½ day per week position for the last month and ongoing. The bones in sidewalk and possibly tipped building images come from a book I just finished on the history of Boton and NY subway building. In the stretch of excavation of Boston Common, a great number of long-forgotten burials were uncovered, the deteriorated bones reburied. In New York, an explosion during tunneling construction resulted in the tipping of a brownstone, vividly described in the book. Reality recombinance – the "stuff of dreams" but not necessarily with any meaning other that extrapolated by one who would claim to "interpret" the dream – that meaning being HIS.]

6/1/14

In the metropolitan Boston area, south of the city itself, there's a huge spread of cemetery. But as I cross the main street in this Hyde Park region, I see that there are no more gravestones. I and a bunch of people I'm with enter what is now really but a park. A sort of granite dish the size of a fountain on a pedestal contains all kinds of pastries and donuts and little bun-less burgers. I tip back the huge plexiglass cover and take a burger.

Next in the back seat of what seems to be a 1940s era car. We're driving through another area of outskirts Boston, Dorchester, where close-set three-deckers line both sides of the street. We drop someone off at one of them and continue on, I'm told, to pick up the driver's son. She mentions that he's been given a thousand dollar award for some academic achievement.

But first we have to drop of her mother who's suddenly the old woman sitting beside me in the back seat of the car. At Columbia Road (just south of Boston's downtown), right against the Southeast Expressway "grandmother" lives in a three-decker. I get out and she sort of leans forward for me to pick her up and lower her to the ground. She's weightless.

The woman driving mentions says that she should pick up her son next. But I ask her to just drop me off in Malden Square [actually about 10 miles north of the dream's locale] which is just the next exit up. I tell her I should head back home as soon as possible, so I'll just ride my bike from Malden square up to Wakefield.

6/15/14

My VW bug parked in an alley, pavement outside wet. Car is piled with books and various cloth (clothing? Bedding?), some of which is falling out onto the street and I'm concerned that the books will be damaged.

Inside the building I'm parked behind, down stairs, into a small pizza-kitchen where Marie [used to me next-door neighbor] is unseen, but I'm told needs directions for someone to get to some place in East Boston. At my car again I've rummaged through the whole confused contents but can't find map-book.

In an upstairs, almost empty dining room at a table with my mother who seems very displeased with me because I haven't been in touch with her for a long time and the while, at college, I've been doing nothing but drinking and screwing-off.

Other tables appear in the room and at them are other people. One group, elderly women and one of them ancient, all stand together and like a cluster a football players bringing down the ball carrier, all fall against a wall with the decrepit woman kind of at the center of the others. At another table I'm suddenly seated with several middle-aged women, trying to explain what I'm doing in life (published some books) and one asks me what I want to be. I answer, cosmologist. No one knows what that means.

At a far table a guy has given me the email address for the East Boston place but there are about twenty numbers and symbols and letters involved and I can't manage to key them into my phone. I tell him I'll wait until I get home and look up the phone number.

A snowy, desolate, street on which I drive uphill in the dark, sensing toward being with my disappointed mother, but also troubled by not knowing if I'll even see her or when I'll get to the summit . . . . if there is one.

6/21/14

High ground/grass expanses with contoured rock exposed/some trees but only in clusters here and there. Distant valley views beyond what seems to be a park or a campus where I am on one of several winding walks. I walk alongside an individual completely concealed in what appear to be brown palm fronds (such as African tribesmen sometimes wear in ceremonies. He's pulling a bicycle-wheeled cart on which, somewhat heaped and entangled, are a whole lot of children.

I leave the park and find myself on a two-lane highway that I know leads down the long, long decline into the valley and finally to the distant city. I sense the urgency of getting there because I haven't finished a basement playroom job for a client and it's been some years. I should really apologize, perhaps even finish the job. I realize that an unheard voice is saying something about 2% being so negligible that there's no need for it to be paid-up or completed.

A bicycle appears for me to ride but as suddenly disappears and I'm walking but with no segue, am inside a large, upper-story chamber and surrounded by commercial washers and dryers and pressing machines and dry-cleaning equipment. The client and his sons are there, soon telling me that I have nothing to finish or worry about because 2% is negligible.

As if the dream has reversed sequence, I'm at the location where the client's house had been but is no more. At least 20 acres including what had been a couple mansions and other very expensive homes have disappeared, leaving a vast pit in the round that resembles a quarry with no stone, or a sand-pit with a lot of loam layers revealed. In this chasm-like depression are numerous little bodies of water, one of them beside a narrow, two-story structure next to a truck weigh-scale. In the water is a hue alligator, its mouth wide open.

But now the opening is into the lower deck on a boat that resembles an old Staten Island ferry. I peer down and see various exercise equipment that, as if being flooded, fills with Negro and Hispanic young men jostling and tussling with each other, getting violent and punching, and expanding from the lower area up towards where I am. I, and others with me, quickly skirt around the vessel on an extremely narrow walkway between structure and a flimsy rail, the fetid waters not too far below. The boat begins to move as we try to escape the melee' moving towards us. It seems that the floating debris and semi-sunken hulls and sagging docks and warehouse ruins and remains beyond are the realm in motion and I, floating and fleeing, am in static state.

7/2/14

In the cab of a tractor trailer rig. With me is one of the other company drivers. We go up a hill on an old highway with nothing visible on either side. But suddenly we're threading our way through an immense, towering thicket in which the roadway is hardly more than a trail. I'm very concerned if we'll find our way out.

Apparently we do, for we're parked behind some stores, other trucks here and there, and one coming around the corner toward us. It's some kind of rubbish collection truck, a little cab section and a bulbous rear compaction unit. It brings my mind of a female spider (tiny head, big egg attached to her body). Somehow I manage to make a u-turn before it blocks our way.

Next, I'm naked and examining what I'd thought to be a natural stone wall beside the road toward the truck terminal building. But I notice star- and other –shaped protrusions from the modules, fitting perfectly into identical-configuration recesses in the adjoining blocks. Obviously, I conclude, this is manufactured stuff. Along the bottom of the wall is an inch or so space between wall and pavement. I begin pouring colorless paint into the crack.

At the terminal building, still naked, I descend a flight of stairs to find someone. I enter a room, previously just open industrial space, that's been nicely made into an apartment complete but for an unfinished (colorless) paint job. Peeking around the corner I see a guy in an inner office, tell him I'm there for a load, and slink back so that he won't see I'm naked.

On a bar or counter next to me there's a (colorless) plaid scarf which I wrap around me. The guy comes into the room and asks me how often I get down from Maine. For some reason I find it difficult to explain to him that I'm stationed in Massachusetts.

7/20/14

An upper floor of an office building and in a large office I'm with a number of other young men and women. It seems like we're awaiting, or have already attended, some kind of recruiting event. On table are pocketbooks and other possessions of the group and perhaps some remnants of refreshments. On a desk there are various scale model locomotives (Lionel steam type), some regular small train-set size, others over a couple feet long.

But then I'm in an adjoining conference room, surrounded by adolescent girls and young women of various nationalities and wearing different costumes. I begin talking, and soon am actually preaching about the meaning of life and essence of Christianity – being for those who can to give for the benefit of those in need. And I proceed to act-out as if I'm Jesus, going around the group as if collecting for the poor and . . . .and then I stop and declare that in our present culture of religion, Jesus would take the money in hand and go over to some bank and borrow a bunch more and spend it all to build a megachurch I which to pray for the sick and starving.

Suddenly the conference room and office seem to be conjoined and several of us are very concerned that we can't make phone calls out to let our parents know why we'll be so late and why we've been incommunicado for so long. An executive-type woman announces that we must immediately leave. As others go toward the stairway I inquire about the model locomotives. No one knows anything about them nor am I able to take any with me.

The stairway down consists of full-floor (no landing) runs and without my feet touching the treads I glide down, my hands sliding along the rails.

The street is full of traffic.

The street becomes full of water, a river flowing around a bend, a tributary coming over a small dam into the main flow. There are a few small rowboats, and in the water are various animals swimming. A cat paddles by and then dives deep out of sight. A pass a donkey doing an in-water somersault. I need to get beyond the bend so that I can reach my destination.

Which may or may not be the vast, low-ceilinged space I'm in next. There may have been a flea market or farmer's market there recently. A few long tables and some collapsed chairs are scattered around. From the shallow trusses which hold up the flat roof wires dangle, some with light sockets, a few with bulbs enough to illuminate the drab interior.

It seems to be my responsibility to strip out the wiring. I unplug one end of a long cord with no problem. But pulling another, from the distant end sparks flicker and I have to search to disconnect the power from the line.

In so doing I find myself with some others outside. One who had been in the place during whatever the event had been, was Bob, a friend from high school days and deceased husband of a dearest friend of mine now. Bob doesn't want to continue taking part in taking the place apart (such as the wiring removal). So he's departed and somehow now on some elongated framework that resembles a bridge – which is at least hundreds of feet up in the sky and drifting slowly away. We watch from the ground, fascinated but alarmed. For Bob is pouring gasoline on one end of the airborne assembly, causing flashes of illumination as if geometries of lightning. What if some aviation regulation (or even NASA) takes notice and he's arrested, we wonder.

But there's nothing we can do and the atmospheric bridge moves ever further away as the flashes become mere flickers.

7/28/14

First I seem to be in an upper floor of the building where my mother was employed when I was a kid 65+ years ago. But the interior is now in ruins and the space strewn and stacked with crates and machinery and desks and more.

A couple of the unseen others who had been working with me are now with me on a motor scooter along with a couple large objects we're in a hurry to deliver somewhere that seems to be in the hilly Dorchester section of Boston.

But the I realize I'm in Lynn heading into Swampscott and on the left side of the road is a washing machine that had been on the motor scooter with me. It's now tipped over on its side, revealing to me someone else's carelessness.

A car stops beside me where I and a couple unseen others stand beside the street. The driver is a woman, rather odd looking, perhaps Philippine or other Indonesian origin. We climb into the back seat and suddenly are parked in a huge lot that seems to be near Lynn Beach, but also resembles a lot at a nearby shopping mall. The woman and I are engaged in a rather heated discussion about beliefs in God. I say that most people's idea of God in contemporary image would be an executive type sitting at a big desk with a glass ashtray on one side and a cigar in it. The woman agrees in that God has to be a person, supernatural, but a person. I launch into a dissertation on God as a system of universal comprehensivity – inclusive of all the parts therein (the "quanta" – but also the whole of the universe/creation (the "field")

She reacts with somewhat annoyed astonishment. She says I really should tell all that to Piaget. [in the dream I realize that when I awake I'll have to go online and look up Piaget.]

I've thanked her for the ride. Now wearing only a bathing suit, I gather up what I assume to be all my clothes and possessions, and I watch her drive away.

I'm suddenly climbing the stairs to the second floor of a 3-decker tenement in which some of my inlaws live. The apartment is a mess, as if only partly lived-in. And at first the only other person there is in the bathroom with the door locked. And I need to use the bathroom. But then I'm in the livingroom area and in horror realize that I didn't take all of my possessions out of the woman's car. And I have no idea who she was.

Further shocked, I realize that I was supposed to be riding my bike up to visit my son, Jack, in Vermont [and a little flash a past dream's scenario of a desecrated industrial city center appears to me for a mere second]. I was supposed to surprise Jack with my visit. I should call him. For it's too late for me to go from Lynn, Mass to Vermont now. I should call my parents to tell them where I am and maybe they can call Jack.

But more horror –my cell phone was, along with my wallet, in my pants which it seems I'd left in the woman's car. But then someone brings me neatly folded clothes: pants, shirt, and a very torn flannel shirt. I'm standing next to a refrigerator which is next to an empty refrigerator with its door open and taller than I. The inside is empty but I assume to be used as a pantry.

Alas, neither phone nor wallet are in my pants.

A little boy smoking a large pipe looks at me with bemused disdain and states that I'll just have to wait and see what happens because there's no alternative.

I look at the badly ripped shirt. No question that it's mine. So the other clothes are too.[I have no cell phone. I have no wallet. I didn't write down the license number. I can't call Jack or my parents. Does this mean that this dream is a premonition that I am soon going to die?

I awake and for a few seconds a sense great anxiety prevails – not concerning that I might die soon. Rather, it's only after I've looked over at the table and seen my phone and wallet neaty placed there that I'm back in reality. And, feeling secure, I slept for another hour and a half before finally getting out of bed and writing this.

July and August, 2014

I find it interesting that for this duration my dreaming either ceased entirely or was just kind of "mental murmurs" that I had no specific imagery-recollection of when I awoke. In proof-read scanning these pages today, I noticed a similar lapse last year.

The only variable I can come up with is length of daylight and temperature. Though for the latter, whatever time of year the interior where I sleep is at about the same.

And for the last couple days here at the end of August, 2014, it's been hotter than the rest of the summer. And yet, suddenly, last night the dream quite vivid when I awoke – which follows here.

I have no more analysis, let alone explanation (the two terms are not synonymous, though sometimes "analysis" does come up with valid causation and understanding). Nor can I imagine any Oedipal or homoerotic or archetypal or other- type psycho-ponders . . . . applicable to the overwhelming content of what I've recorded of my dreams herein.

I don't deny all the "classical-school" assumptions may be applicable to some dreams (wish-fulfillment, phallic symbolism, etc). Of some people.

But damned if any of that mainstream stuff fits my dreamscapes.

The only possible perspective of perspicacity in my estimation – yes, the title of this book . . . . . . Scavenging the Landfill of the Unconscious.

9/1/14

On a sloping, paved area behind various buildings. Some seem to be three-decker housing with decrepit porches rising above. Others are only one story, apparently the backs of stores or shops with rubbish containers and rubbish not all in the containers around their doorways. Apparently I'm supposed to do some kind of repair work on one of the buildings.

But I'm being pursued! And when I'm just about to be overtaken, I lie down flat on the ground with my hands over my head. I must have been able to prove my purpose for being in the area.

Suddenly I'm walking through a snowy city center, very indistinct, somehow known to be such – which leads me onto a sidewalk beside a park. Back within the lawns there's a building, perhaps an aquarium. People are around, including a cop who materializes before me. I'm now on a motor scooter and he's pointing a radar gun at me. I must not be speeding, for he disappears. But I wonder that he didn't cite me for driving a motor vehicle on the sidewalk.

On a bit, a broad curve in the road, ocean on my left, and a garden apartment complex ahead. Realizing that I'm now being pursued from the ocean, possibly by pirates, I race into the complex parking area, jump off the scooter, and run to the back of one of the buildings. I climb stairs to an upper deck and, just as the pursuers are gaining on me, I push it loose from the building.

For it's now afloat like a raft, and although there's attempt to swim after me, I manage to propel it away from any danger.

10/14,15,16

I'm in the cab. Behind is a trailer full of stone or gravel. Extremely heavy I start To pull forward and realize that something's wrong. There's not the sense of resistance that such a load would create. I glance through the cab's rear window and realize that the trailer hasn't hooked and is just about to slid off the cab. If that happened I'd have to call and pay for a massive crane to pick it up so I could back under it again. I shift into reverse, gun the engine a little, and the trailer hooks.

Then I'm talking to one of the other drivers who's telling me that yet another driver has died, but even though dead was driving his rig in the cemetery and ran over his own grave, causing his corpse to be actually projected out of the squished crypt and, like a gelatinous clump of decay, shot all the way out over the cemetery wall into the woods beyond..

I'm sitting on a bench. There appears to be the back of a ball park score board structure in front of me. But that dissolves to reveal a court room. I must be in the jury section. Beyond a rail there's a man in a three piece suit. He must be a lawyer. I say to him, "You look like a lawyer". He asks me, "you have a problem with lawyers?" I reply, "anyone who wants to criticize lawyers to their face should state that they've been inspired by New Yorker Magazine lawyer cartoons – and the prestige of the publication should prevent the lawyer from being offended."

(none of this conversation was "heard" in the dream – only realized)

I'm in a car going up hill behind a tractor-trailer rig. One of the doors of the trailer is partially open and I want to inform the driver because freight might fall out. But at the crest of the hill he turns left and I have to go right. And that leads me downhill and I come into a huge, sprawling intersection (think Times Square greatly enlarged).

But then I'm alone. It's night, damp. I seem to have come through some area strewn and stacked with derelict equipment and vehicles. But I've reached my destination which is an auto repair garage owned and operated by the guy who used to own the glass company where I lived (actually). I need to have something fixed though I seem to be on foot.

The place seems to be closed. It's the middle of the night. But peering through the plate glass I see the outline of a child in the dark. And soon a garage door opens on the side of the building and a couple men emerge. Then the owner comes out through the front door.

11/13/14

    I'm in the second floor tenement apartment of inlaws. Need to use the bathroom badly. It's latched from inside – but in no time my teen age niece comes out. I go in. She hasn't flushed the toilet but it makes no difference because I just add mine to hers.

11/16/14

    Racing along a wide, undulating beach. Wrecked equipment here and there.

    On what seems to be a pier high above the water – but also an elevated transit structure. Attached to me are a number of tiny tubes all conjoined at a sort of hub. The image is from an EKG I had recently, wires rather than tubes. I'm searching for a place where I can remove the tubes, for to do so I'll have to be naked. I find a sort of electrical closet but a watchman comes along. He doesn't see me.

    Out on the pier there are stacks of shipping containers but they're not metal. They're huge margarine boxes fastened to wooden pallets. It seems I'm supposed to deliver one of them via truck.

    In a warehouse, upper floor, realizing how creepy it would be to be there alone at night. But there's activity as men on forklifts slide masses of intermixed lumber along the floor. Before leaving the building I'm trying to get a Hispanic guy to sing something – but he's resisting and becoming aggravated so I stop and let him leave. I'm now outside and the building is only one floor high but extending a great distance, part of it in ruin. I'm with a number of the drivers from work and we're waiting for the coffee truck to arrive. Under the rear portion of the building there's a basement, its windows boarded, for two people died therein from some chemical leak and the whole section is secured as a Hazmat site.

    The Mass Pike or some other highway is on the other side of a tall fence that consists of side-by-side poles, about 8' high, shaped like skinny humans shoulder-to-shoulder. It's become the site of "graffiti mayhem", for all along there are people chalking and painting the poles to look like they're wearing clothing or uniforms – and to have faces and expressions, etc. For occupants of the houses all along the other side of the street from the poles, the art work is a nightmare, ruining their property values.

    Inside someone's house I'm asked for the time and being reminded that I'm wearing a watch, hold up my arm for him to see. I've forgotten how to tell time.. He seems to be some elected official, and mentions that the artists should simply be arrested. I suggest that he should get a gun. But then I consider that the opposite reaction might work better. Really promote the pole-painting as a community artwork event. Kind of analogous, I say, to inner cities designating certain walls and surfaces as "canvases" for graffiti taggers to legally embellish. And I conclude, if each and every post were painted, such a crowd of Nutcracker-Suite toy-soldier configurations would just become an extent and expanse of visual variable perhaps even resembling camouflage patterns.

11/23/14

    I've driven through what almost seems like a maze of alleys. On each side of the narrow passageways are the fronts of buildings that once may have been row houses. But windows on the street level there are no doors or windows or stairs. Each of their front walls has been opened up to provide for freight delivery into the building. Many of those openings are now blocked by what seem to be ramps, hinged at the bottom, and drawn up over the opening like drawbridges. Here and there some are opened down, thus serving as delivery docks. I can see vaguely within the openings. The interiors are stuffed with toppled and strewn recycling materials, broken machinery and appliances, and much that is unrecognizable mess.

Outside, along the alleys, there are pieces of machinery, some electric and resembling partially disemboweled metallic rats, their cords as if tails.

I'm suddenly on a bicycle. I'm looking for my Toyota pickup truck. I'd driven far into this industrial wasteland and parked where the zone bordered what seemed to be a cemetery overgrown into a forest.

I'm anxious, pedaling up and down and across the alleys. Ethnic indivduals glard at me or smile. One of them spray painting a satellite dish which has been affixed as a top to a combination pressure cooker and wok

In the distance I can see the remains of what must have been a 6 story wood framed factory building. It's being demolished, the blackened and fractured planks and beams stacked on trailers to be taken away somewhere. Using what I can see of the remaining three floors of the building as a landmark, I turn around 180 degrees and head back into the midst of the labyrinth. I should now be able to find my pickup truck.

11/27/14

Up a drive with views of fields on one side, perhaps an orchard on the other. I come to a little enclave that could be a residential cul de sac or the courtyard of some religious organization. It seems to be the latter, for several older men are gathered in the driveway to a columned building and are about to sacrifice a child who, for some reason, has not met the standards of the cult.

Between the stone walls beside the pavement, the little boy is crying, and the men are hesitant. But it seems some divine order requires that they carry out the killing. I walk past the group, feeling helpless, guilty, horrified. But up the stairs and into the building I find a fine Thanksgiving feast laid out buffet-style and help myself.

Back outside, the child is still alive, elders' discussion now heated. I walk down the sloping road to where I'd parked my Oldsmobile. A quick look out at the vista of the fields and farmland and I turn the key.

I've just left the building (again) where the Thanksgiving dinner was served. I walk down the granite steps, look down at the driveway between the stone walls. The men are there, but the child is gone. For a moment I fear he's been sacrificed.

But as I walk toward the Oldsmobile the toddler comes running up the hill to me and almost leaps into my arms, snuggling. I'm moved almost to tears and tell him how glad I am he's still alive. He babbles something to the effect of agreement. I reluctantly let him go and he runs on up the hill.

I'm in the Olds. It doesn't start. I put it in neutral and let it roll down the hill and out onto the road where I manage to back to the side.

At that point, my late wife Angie and a couple of our kids (very young age) are in the car which is running and I'm driving and we're heading toward where a friend of years ago lived in Rhode Island. As we drive, Angie is telling me that Diana (my first wife) had called while I was "at church" (up above). She'd warned Angie that my friend's place was really "80%" and to be prepared for that level of deprivation and socio-economic dearth. My ex-wife has actually become very wealthy. But my old friend's place was beautiful.

At any rate, we wind through rural areas where there are old mills and factories but no place to turn around until finally I'm in the parking lot and playground (combined) of a school that looks like a warehouse. We're able to turn around and thus find our way to my friend's Rhode Island estate.

Happy Thanksgiving.

11/30/14

I'm supposed to be playing piano at some bar or restaurant. I'm driving in the dark toward the place, but realize I don't know where I'm supposed to be going. It's dark out. Should I have first stopped at the trucking terminal and picked up a trailer load to be delivered to the place before I began my performance?

I turn, go down a steep hill and into and then out of a parking lot of a decrepit warehouse. It's closed, perhaps even abandoned. On downhill there's a sort of dead-end cluster of streets with three-decker tenement houses crowded all around. I have no idea where I am.

But suddenly I'm on foot in the middle of an intersection of at least five main streets. Vehicles and pedestrians are everywhere, some having to avoid me as I walk. I want to ask where I am but since I don't know where I'm supposed to be going, it seems that there's no sense in knowing where I am.

It's the same situation as I find myself inside a municipal building. Offices are behind glass partitions and access doors on each side of a corridor. I need to get a message to my uncles who employ me at their masonry supply company and expect me to be at work, or at least playing the piano at a restaurant or bar, or also delivering something there.

I have no phone. I can't ask anyone anything. They're all foreigners.

Then in a vast vacant lot I stand alone and my cell phone rings. It's my long passed-away relative from South Carolina, "Uncle" Len. I ask about "Aunt Mae" and find out she's well. But their daughter, Jane, has been diagnosed with some sort of cancer and the prognosis isn't good. I'm very concerned, since, as I tell him, so have I. But 100% of my inpatient medical costs are usually covered, I'm not concerned, even though the actual organ in which I have the cancer was misdiagnosed at first.

Len then tells me that Jane's husband had left the country on some clandestine military assignment and now can't get back in because there was no record of his having left, so perhaps he's faking who he is to try to regain entry to the U. S. It's been a problem for Jane, what with her cancer, but the guy as been able to buy a luxury vehicle and he enjoys challenging others where he is to races. He's won quite a bit of money. And he should be able to sell the car at a profit and then be able to bribe his way back into the country to be with his wife in time for her surgery.

> [quite a bit of the above was the result of my reading extensive material on cancer treatment and medical facilities in a Boston Globe Sunday Supplement. Descriptions of city areas appear in the dream. Jane is a Cousin with whom I talk a couple times a year. She was brain injured In an auto accident, but cancer would have been worse. And as in the

other dreams in this collection, this one is a "landfill" of bits and pieces of image and idea almost randomly conjoined into a "night-continuum".]

12/22/14   had sent G 1st seg. Of Anya, and re-read it myself

    I've come in from a very long run and parked the truck I drive. After sleeping, I want to resume my trip, but find the truck is gone. Someone else has taken it. I ask when it'll be back. It won't. It's going to be scrapped. I'm very upset because I have all kinds of belongings and writings in it. I'll have to go to where the other driver has taken it. At least I can retrieve my irreplaceable possessions and papers. It may have gone to Concord, NH. There's a company terminal there. I've had insufficient sleep. I can't take another truck on a run to Concord. I have to go as on personal business..
    1st, walking along street. Area resembles Dot. Ave. down near the T station. On the right a one-story, decrepit building, Seems to be some kind of social center. People outside but only inside recognizable as older, working-class types. Seated on benches along each sides of a big main area. Someone unseen beside me informs me they're praying.
    Out another door into a hallway. Bunch of people. I walk through them and am headed toward the street. I hear my name called, think I must be mistaken, but again. I turn. A middle-aged woman is coming toward me and I walk toward her. We enter the hallway and address the men standing there, at first mistaking them for kids I knew when I was in high school. But I realize they can't be. They're in their middle age.
    One asks my age after I tell them of my mistaken identification of them. I have to figure from when I graduated from high school to the present. One of the guys tells me he graduated when he was 22. I tell him I was 18.
    As I walk away from the building, what's behind me turns into a street in Somerville that goes steeply uphill and dead-ends at a function hall. Beside me now on the corner of it and an avenue there's a funeral parlor in a decrepit building. Parked beside the curb are two hearses, one of them actually protruding slightly into the avenue. I consider that, congested with no one around, when a function and funeral are going on at the same time, things must really get hectic
    On a roof of a lower room off the back of some big 3-decker building. A bench along the edge of the very rear. Bunch of people around. One is a young man with some kind of straps with buckles that he wants to be able to put together as one longer one. A woman who seemed to be my late wife, Angie, at a young age sits with the bench.
    The strap guy sends someone else in to the building itself where some sort of gathering of people is taking place. Whatever is obtained is working to joint the straps into one. Angie and I lean forward, kind of tipping the bench as we do. A priest or minister approaches and we agree to tell him we're praying. Seen inside the bench where a portion of the cover lifts are office supplies.

12//24/14

I'm naked. I'm in a back room with a very high ceiling and tall windows. The rear wall is bowed. There's the feeling being in the town house where I lived for aa while when I was in college.

The door is closed to the front area, but I'm aware that there's a gathering of young people there.

I 'm desperate to get out of where I am without being found.

The floor of the room has become dirt with sparse growth and erosion, as if a steep field descending toward the within. I throw blankets down just a bit, and a couple pieces of small hardware fall with them. I have to retrieve everything, for the little parts will fit something I'll need – or become.

Outside the rear wall an embankment rises as if it's a continuation of the floor inside. I struggle to get my blankets and now some clothes up and onto the level surface which on which railroad tracks run.

Up on the tracks I push my possession so that they can't be seen from the windows just in time. The group from the front is coming into the back where I was.

I'm in another building. It seems to house a monastery, or maybe a military organization. An unseen older man is taking charge of me now that I've entered, and the next thing I know I'm in a huge area like a one-story conference or assembly room. On each side a ladder rises to an opening in the suspended ceiling.

Now recognized as a hooded monk, my escort is ordering me to climb the ladder into the space above. I'm up the ladder almost all the way and being told that I'm fortunate to have chosen that ladder. It would take me to a place of owning property. Had I gone up the other, I would have been imprisoned and subject to torture for two years.

But suddenly I've gone down to a lower level, apparently in the same building. Several young men in military fatigues are there, a couple playing ping-pong. The monk gets their attention by announcing, "Here's another one."

Naked still, feeling strange, I'm among them and others who appeared and we all are gathered at a table that encircles a vertical support beam for the floor above. One of the guys needs an umbrella. There's discussion of his having invented it, a unique model, but not having made any money out of it. Another man joins the group, having come from a separate section the building. He's carrying an umbrella which is appears as if it's been blown "inside out" but a violent wind. But by shaking it, he gets it back to normal.

A voice of subdued outrage is heard: "He's taken my idea. That was my invention of an umbrella".

Crouched and naked in a crowded supermarket. I'm blocking an aisle, so there's a line like stalled traffic of people with grocery carts having to go around me to get to the checkout. My shopping stuff has spilled out of my cart and I'm scurrying around picking up the various items. I realize I have to get out of the aisle and move so people can get by me on both sides. But my stuff is still strewn. But at least I'm somewhat concealed under a display counter or shelf.

,

12/25/14

Where I am is uncertain, but there are various junked vehicles and pieces of equipment on one side of an alley, and a huge, brick, derelict building on the other. I seem to be with one of my grandsons, waiting to have my hair cut so that I can get home to my parents. The hair cutter appears and is a business partner I used to have. Before he can start on my hair he has something to do and disappears. And I wait, And wait.

Finally I can wait no more and leave the ally, cross a shallow, overgrown ravine, and climb up the other side onto a road.

I'm inside a cavernous bay in a concrete building. Perhaps heavy equipment was repaired there, but it seems to have been abandoned for some time. There are strews of trash and leaves all over, coagulations of them in corners and against support girders. Someone is saying things about how nice the owners had been and that the job was good to have,

But then, in a different part of the building I'm supposed to be modernizing and preparing the building to be used as office or medical space. There are protrusions of pipes and hanging from the ceiling all kinds of metallic things that might have held pulley-wheels back in time. To cover all the crap and fixtures and hangings and protrusions I realize is going to be almost overwhelming.

I leave the building and, preoccupied, am crossing the street without looking. The canteen truck almost hits me. The driver is good natured, but admonishes me about my carelessness. He parks in front of the building and people come out to buy sandwiches and such. There's a young man among them who seems far different from the others who are "working-class" types. The food truck man mentions to me that the young man will have an interesting future.

In a room that seems to be in a tenement building. I'm tipping something toward me on top of a bureau. It may be a stereo component, for on top of it is a stereo component which is going to fall toward me. I stop tipping. On the porch outside this room a woman (seems to be my late wife) has been and continues yelling all kinds of invective and threatening punishment unto torture.

I've heard all I can tolerate and go out on the porch. Looking devastated, crouched on a chair, is my stepdaughter. She hurts so much, but used to it, I know.

I yell at the yeller.

"You know, it sounds like the Gestapo out here!!!"

1/1/2015

It's in Maine. A ramshackle, rambling cottage on a gravelly stretch of land is not far above sea level. I've been visiting the people there, or working on the place fort them. I'm leaving, my hatchback car loaded so much I can just barely fit in the last object. I go back inside to get yet another something, and say goodbye to the unseen others,

Outside, I wish I'd gotten a sweater out of my suitcase, but too much trouble now.

I notice the tires need air. I consider that I should have added oil to the engine.

But I'm on the way and on a bicycle and going up a steep hill. On the left the land rises even more. Tied to a tree are two creatures that resemble pony-size hyenas, but just seem passively curious as I go by. I realize they're some kind of dog – or deer. Now on a bicycle, I'm off the steep road on the right side. An undulating expanse of grass is there, all the way to the crest. When I get to the top, I realize I've left my baseball bat back down the hill and turn around and go back. It's gone. Someone must have taken it.

At the top, the uphill way ends at a cross street. Concerned about air for my tires (car of bike at this point seem to be the same thing), I look to the left. Not far past several large houses, there seems be a little commercial section and then the ocean.

I head to the right and find myself in a vehicle with a several others, a couple of them middle aged women. We watch as a man exits another vehicle, crosses the road carrying a commercial coffee maker, and dumps the contents out in the field. I comment that he's illegally disposing of hazmat and I wish I had a placard to confront him with.

We've turned around and one of the women asks if a passing car is an electric. I conduct a brief and detailed lesson re. alternative automotives: first, that one's not electric (it looked like a mid-eightees Buick), also that it's too early for implementing all electric which will need nationwide "charging stations" (not filling) – but hybrid will be the car of the future – the drive train no more, for four electric motors, one for each tire, will do away with all the weight and friction and pollution of the internal combustion, mechanical drivetrain "conventional" cars.

We've gone down a hill and I find myself alone where the street ends, just past a commercial district straight out of Maine. I'm now desperate to find somewhere to fill my tires, but the view out over the bay into the receding arc of shoreline afar is beautiful and distracts me for a bit.

But I have to get from there to wherever I'm supposed to be going.

Or is it that all that was symbolic of the past – and I've arrived at what wasn't then but is to be now, even though there is deflation and, to add symbol to image, the bat is gone?

2/20/15
Fragments: inside an assembly-hall sized area where there's a single counter with a glass front through which I'm able to see donuts. I select a sugar-coated one, but the proprietresse of the place tells me that it's as hard as a rock. So I don't take it.

Another area which resembles ruins of a couple stories of concrete building. I'm on an upper level. Below me there seems to be a cavernous space, empty, partly underground, and filled with water. Standing on a lower level is a disheveled, middle-aged man, his stomach bulging out of his unbuttoned suit jacket. He's telling me of his failure as a traveling salesman, and that he has no means of transportation and perhaps I could take him to Route 128 in Peabody on my bicycle. I feel bad for him.

2/21/15
It might have been where the last remaining, partially destroyed, structure had been part of a military base, or an industrial complex. Through the property runs a single rail line, obviously unused for ages, and stretching, weed-filled, out into undiscernable

distance through flat marshland. I walk across the tracks, around the building, and enter my car which had been parked on the far side, out of sight.

Back on the other side of the building, I'm standing outside, examining what seems to be both myself and an adult-sized infant in a diaper. I remove two safety pins and am a bit shocked that I/it has no penis – rather, a tiny protruberance (less than an "angry inch") with a droplet of liquid like a finial on its end.

Then I'm on a bicycle along a sidewalk along a street and on the other side of a cross-street there are a couple tables set up. On them are various antique telephone and radio equipment, modules and parts. Also some artistic objects. I ask a young boy standing nearby if the stuff is for sale or for the taking. He says to take what I want. Alone at first, with intent to take all, I'm suddenly just one of small crowd picking objects. But I manage to scoff a vintage phone bell module and place it in the back seat of my (now) car.

\

3/23/15
A small pond is down in somewhat of a pit of the surrounding scraggly, rocky shores. It seems I've been sleeping on the opposite bank from where I'm now climbing up, looking at snarled roots intertwined with rocks and semblances of organic insinuations. Nothing feels creepy or ominous, but the area is unsettling.

I'd parked my pickup truck at the crest of this trail from the pond. I wonder, as I climb, why I hadn't slept in it.

Suddenly I see what remains of it – hardly four feet consisting of the very front and behind that what looks like it had been both mashed and bitten off. A pair of deep, muddy ruts from the pond reveals that something, perhaps a monster or vehicle on monster size tires, had done the damage.

I'm thinking that now I'll have to go to the Chevy dealer and buy a Chevy Spark.

But, still asleep, I next realize that I'm sleeping and there's no chance that my truck is damaged, for the only body of water anywhere near is out back of the trailer I'm in.

4/1/15

The interior of a huge store, most of the space under a towering ceiling taken up by crowded corridors of merchandise of all kinds on counters. On one side there is a sort of balcony or mezzanine level above the ground floor. And to the upper level of this area, also crowded with merchandise, that I've followed to chattering Negro women.

But suddenly I'm seated across my living room from my adult son, Jack. He's dressed in an expensive suit. I'm in bathrobe and holding a drink and telling him that even though I drink I'm productive because I'm multi-tasking while I sip. I'm writing, for example. And then I've approached him and he me and we're discussing how there's a perimeter around a person – a sort of "safe-zone", perhaps two feet. This should be mutual distance so that people aren't in each other's faces and appearing combative.

Back in the store I find myself, on the lower level toward the rear section of the left half. The shoe section is there and I note the salesmen. One, a tiny man who seems just right for such a menial position. But others, also dressed in suits, are tall and their faces reveal that they should have had the opportunity to be outdoorsmen or tradesmen and to dress in work clothes. Still in the back section, I've wandered around a sort of valley in the between walls.

There, a number of men are in groups of a couple or several, and seem to be discussing something about a stage production. I find myself clinging to a steel column that rises in to the heights. I let myself collapse, embracing it. I'm wailing that this is the closing and I'm coming to the end.

But suddenly in a corridor on the mezzanine level, it's revealed to me that being guaranteed fast legal procedure and resolution is often a lie. One has to pull the documents so stating out from the wall where they're pinned. Behind them, proof is on very thin foam sheets that one pulls up from behind lower wall coverings to where they can be seen behind where the documents were.

Beyond, still on that level, I watch two young women with very bright (color unseen but realized) red lipstick. They've been arguing over some items of whieh there was only one of a kind – which both wanted. But suddenly they resolve the dispute and full-frontal kiss each other, jump back as if shocked, and exclaim loudly, "ooooopppps !!" (In the dream I realize sound but don't hear it).

Back downstairs and on the far side. I'm with a crowd who are leaving the building. They look like college students. They seem to separating into two groups. I join one while some in the other make disparaging remarks about my not being able to afford to be with them. All of us in the group I'm in have put strapped little four-wheeled (like old-fashioned roller skates) devices to our feet. We roll out the several side-by-side doors, down steps, across a sidewalk and street and on the other side, those with me watch with interest to see if I'll be able to make the jump between the street and a ramp, about a two inch vertical difference. I'm successful and we all roll on toward a park.

There, are lawns and plantings in plots separated by a kind of rectilinear network of walkways. The walk we're on, like the others, is concrete, this one recently poured, but "set" sufficiently that we're not damaging it by rolling in it. But it's still uncured enough that the bunch of us, rolling along, are able to use rake-like devices we have to fine-finish the surface.

I see this whole scenario now as if from apart. And though park and cement walks and casually dressed young people with rakes (where tines would be, bristles attached) . . . . I see what I realize is almost a "collage of disparate visual fragments re-composed into a composite based on the theme of a hockey game.

4/1/15

The warehouse is at the top of a steep ramp. I've backed the rig up against one of the loading doors. I'm out of the truck and starting to walk down to the office to turn in paperwork when I notice the truck's creeping forward, turning toward me to the right. My first panicked thought is whether I should run around the front (the shortest distance) to jump into the cab, or around the back of the trailer (the safer way since the other way the truck, moving faster now, would be heading for me and possibly run me over.

I've been running alongside it as it continues rolling, now onto a side drive toward an upper parking area. It starts to turn that way, but almost in slow motion rolls over onto its side, tractor and both.

Next I'm walking up from the office with some company official. He's handing me a piece of paper with the name of a lawyer I was already supposed to have been in touch with for some reason. At the top of the hill we're in another office where I can't provide him with my company card or its number – only my social security number, which he doesn't want. I leave to go to the lower office.

On the way down I seem to be up high above the ramp I'd backed the rig up originally. From my elevation to the ramp there's a sloped wall of boulders, some snow-covered. I kind of jump and slide down the boulders. On the ramp I see my son Richard, but the scene shifts suddenly and I'm seeing him behind the rig he's backed up the hill at the end of his run. His trailer doors are open and the freight he's picked is all the way to the rear, floor to ceiling.

And then Richard and I are walking down the ramp. His hands are full with briefcase and a coat and his day's paperwork. So I'm carrying the rest of what he's taking home with him – one object being a commercial glass door which thus seems something like a transparent, long, very thin suitcase. At the lower office, I lean it against a wall while Rich checks out and punches the time clock

Apparently on a section of Lebanon Street in Melrose, Rich is complaining that I don't spend enough time with him. I'm on a bicycle and swerve up onto the sidewalk to avoid the approach of a huge roadbuilding-type vehicle with a blade under it. I yell that I have to spend time with my wife.

Next, sitting across a table from a young yuppie type man. His toddler son is babbling amazing nonsense sounds as names of the various objects pictured on what seems to be some kind of bank literature. The older son shares some kind of pastry with they younger. I notice the older has tattoos on his arm, and hope they aren't permanent, for he's hardly 5 himself.

I'm at my kitchen sink and alarmed because nothing is coming out of the sprayer even though I know it's full of fluid.

4/2/15

My wife and I are in bed, holding hands, very romantic. But something about her lacking secretion requires that a small nail be used. But by just hammering nothing is accomplished. I suggest a pneumatic nailer. She agrees. The first try misses. The second seems to work, but must have gone throughher and out, and it ricochets around the far end of the room for many seconds, to our amusement.

We hear the doorbell. I'm suddenly alarmed that I'm going to be late for the part-time work I've just started. Downstairs I see the front door open and a little elf-like creature is running from me into the kitchen, then dining room, and around toward the front door and I reverse direction to confront it – but it goes down into the cellar. I look in every nook and cranny but can't find it. Angie (wife) and I are then affixing some scrap screen to cover the front door opening. And then it's canvas or plastic that she and I and others are trying to unrumpled to fasten to a shed roof,

The job I've taken is at a trucking company. I'm to move trailers and once and awhile deliver freight. All their equipment is junk. Their yard is a vast, dirt and rock field.

I've punched in and gone to find the tractor I'll drive. A NEMF (company I used to work for in reality) rig comes racing into the yard and stops at the far end. I find a tractor.

It seems to be the next day and I'm a half hour late getting to the job. But since the management in the office also have something to do with my legal affairs and they're real estate agents, I say nothing and no one seems to notice. I get paperwork, exit the office, climb down from that level to the ground by the steps provided in a huge pallet of packages of sliced ham, some of which are scattered on the ground. I consider taking some for lunch.

4/3/15

Two single lanes with narrow strip of underbrush and intermittent trees between them. Straight into the vanishing point of distance. Dismal, Ominous. Not another vehicle in sight

Atop a hill that I recognize from a dream long ago, but the ramshackle buildings are missing now. Just a junkyard perspective of wrecked vehicles of all kind including heavy commercial equipment I'm trying to back my van into a space but can't see behind me.

A valley with extremely steep, rocky hillside rising one side. Overpass of an interstate highway is on the other side of me and it seems that I've exited from that highway, which, itself, might have been the narrow two-lanes of the first part of the dream. Up from the valley a narrow trial, paved by blacktop, winds. I see no one else. I ascend.

And find myself on the very wide, and quite dream-distorted, resemblance of Blue Hill Avenue through the Mattapan section of Boston. This broad avenue with a stark, unplanted center strip, passes through a section of the city that was once somewhat elite, but has now degenerated and crime-ridden. Where the avenue is actually level for a stretch after the descent from the Franklin Park section, in the dream it seems almost as steep as a ski jump, but avenue-wide (six lanes). On this rise some kind of Biblical/historical movie is being filmed. Water (for a flood effect?) is being released and cascading down the slope. Actors and props and camera equipment are being upset and swept along down with the deluge. At the foot of the slope where there's an actual main intersection, in the dream the water has accumulated to the extent of a vast lake. I see things floating and partially submerged, but there's no evidence of disaster or calamity. Perhaps all is part of the plot?

4/4/15

At first it seems I'm one of a row of beds that are side-by side, each having blankets and or sheets and or spreads sort of rolled up on each side from head to foot. My mother is at the far end of the one I'm on and she's shouting about some "class impropriety" the postman has committed by trespassing beyond the dock.

And I notice that far end of what I thought were beds all come to a point like prows. And what I thought were blankets on the sides are actually gunwales. And I'm on one of a row of boats which, I now realize, are actually undulating up and down because they're afloat and against a pier. I'm appalled that my mother would be so pompous and elitist, yet vocally crude and loud.

Suddenly I'm in a cellar area of a commercial building. I see that I've entered from what appears to be Commercial Street in Malden, and I'm at the rear of the basement of the building. One of the previous terminal managers of the company I worked for [actually] seems to be either the proprietor or salesman of the enterprise that occupies the area. The merchandise reminds me of what they sell in import stores – brass trinkets, woven baskets, some fabrics, statuettes. I'm interested in a little urn-like filigree on legs into which one inserts a CD or DVD and something happens as a result.

Though the whirling of a room full of hoop-skirted women doesn't seem to have a connection with the demonstration disc that was put in the devise, that's what I'm dreaming next. I watch the skirts whirl, all of them pleated, and the pleats as if teeth on rounded, trapezoidal gears (small diameter at top and large at bottom). It looks like the skirts are all meshing parts of a machine – reminding me of the beginning images of Lionsgate Films.

A two story brick building to my left. Either was or is to be office space or a school. It's either being renovated or built. On my right is a long stretch of chain link fence. Beyond that is a vast open space. I'm on a bike, seeing no one to ask about the place. But suddenly Mike [actual former work associate] is walking along the wall that the fence is atop. We stop side-by-side. I mention being glad I'm not working any more, having to be in the cold. He admits his displeasure that he'll still have to work many years. Have to get up at 4 in the morning. Get out in the 20 degree cold. Get to work and have to work all day.

****

4/9/15

It almost appears that I've driven my massive tractor-trailer rig up a narrow trail and into a small woodsy park atop a hill. To continue on to the house delivery that's my destination, I have to make a wide swing and turn between two gate posts. They're at the end of the drive up to the unseen, but assumed, mansion.

I'm apparently within it, in a room with many others, mostly women of different ages. I'm looking for a surface on which to spread out various documents and paperwork, finally finding a narrow table next to a sofa. Seated on the sofa is a girl, perhaps late-teenage. She reaches over and whisks everything I've put on the table off onto the sofa beside her, gets up, and departs. I pick things up, noticing that now I'm missing two checks made out to me. Finding her mother, I say that we need to confront the girl so I can get my checks back.

Walking along beside a deserted highway, but with a car parked here and there along it. My adult son is with me and notices an object on the ground. He picks it up and we're both amazed and amused. It's a huge "butt plug" (used for anal sex play) which is attached to a plastic jar. He's still carrying it when we enter the hospital corridor where he places it on a counter and it transforms into a kind of cross between an antique doll with highly expressive face and dressed in fine fabrics – and a bobble-head doll, about 4' tall. This figurine makes faces at the people passing.

At the end of the corridor we're directed into a room with a long conference table. We open our lunches and start eating. Interns and doctors and others start coming in and we're forced all the way to the end of the table. There, I continue eating while reading a copy of The Economist which I'm holding along with a Metropolitan Boston Yellow Pages.

Finished with our meal, we depart the room and I first locate a men's room and with great relief relieve myself.

At a desk I'm told that I'll have to go to another department to get a replacement of the missing check. Walking back the corridor it's remarkable how crowded it's become.

4/10/15

I'm with someone else. It seems that he's a friend from my childhood with whom I've kept in touch through the decades. But I don't see him. But I know both he and I are looking for a men's room. We're behind the backs of four or five story brick buildings. Their specter is as if perhaps ready for demolition. At least they're rather degenerated, fire escapes sagging and parts missing, some windows boarded.

There's a door with a "men's " sign on it. Someone's already in it. Neither my companion or I can wait. He relieves himself behind some piece of debris. I come around the corner to where the buildings don't extend back so far. There, in a row in the open air, are several toilets of antique vintage. I realize there must have been a restroom containing them which was torn down from around them.

We continue on the swath of land behind the buildings. A road's width if must have been for access to deliver to the buildings. For that width, the way is rutted and then actually undulated as if by erosion, water filling the depressions. Parts of ruined equipment, growths of gnarled shrubs, and snarls of grass and weeds are along the way. Beside it, plant growth and trees assert themselves.

At the end of the stretch of buildings we emerge up and onto a sidewalk. At a short distance in each direction we see buildings. But for a span in front of us there's a view in which includes a bridge and the river it crosses I realize that I have come onto Commonwealth Avenue just West of the Boston University buildings. The river is the Charles. The bridge, once known as the "Cottage Farm Bridge" is the B. U. bridge.

As we stand there, two young women come along. One is wearing something that encloses her head and in a way resembles a bag. But I realize it's a bonnet or cowl and no doubt part of a religious or cultural costume of which her ankle length skirt is evidence. Unheard as sound, their voices are of foreign words, apparently German.

On aways we're on a swath of land to the right of which at first there seemed to be a towering cliff of sandstone. But almost emerging in the image there are openings small deck-size openings all over this elevation, each with a rail and fencing below. We see the sliding glass doors that access these areas from the inside of what we realize are apartment or condominium buildings. At one time the structures must have extended in greater depth that encompassed where we are walking. There are foundations segments evident, and myriad debris such as broken bricks and glass shards. I realize that something like a huge knife must have just sliced off the greater depth of the buildings. And thereafter the patio-openings had been provided for.

On further we are higher than any surrounding buildings. Almost as if atop a knoll. For but a second there seems to be a stretch of seaside amusement park walkway, a counter with fried dough, some toss to win games.

Nothing but the knoll and one shrub that resembles a drastically skimpy Christmas tree almost totally dried up to mere twigs. Tied within them is a young woman who at first is asking me for money. I tell her I have none, but she should be thankful that I kept her from getting in trouble. We had both worked, she picking the freight orders, I loading them in my truck – at a place that made plastic housewares.

She is attractive. But I feels nothing sexually.

CONCLUSION

It's occurred to me, "with dreams like these, who needs to watch TV or rent movies?" A somewhat epic scope, almost kaleidoscopic, of conception has truly entertained my nights. I hope this brief span will amuse, intrigue, and even fascinate those who will read this book.

Though in dreams the spelunk-scavenging from the experiential landfill may be most eclectic, when wide awake my mind has mined extremes of image and emotion just as creative, concatenative, . . .off the wall. I've written it in some of my fiction.

One doesn't have to dream to activate the "dream-state" of idea and image.

One doesn't have to be awake to mentally process inference, inspiration, interpretation, even unto artistic and even intellectual formulation.

In my experience there's a conceptual continuum of which dreams content and creativity (per se) are not only complementary, but actually derive from significantly the same neuro-dynamics, even domains, of the mind/brain. Awake, there's a format of functionality involved to contain the content or
direct the flow of thought-dynamics. The dream can drift, whirl, eddy.

But obvious in actual creativity (especially science fiction writing and graphics), while wide awake, there's the potential of the mind's meanders even into absolute mayhem including apocalyptic carnage and creatures.

This sample of my dream-creativity should suffice to publish. But hopefully I'll dream on (and likely keep taking notes).

As for my awake-state creativity, search Books by Appleton Schneider for the range of subjects and titles. And I hope the extravaganza of my mind will fuse with that of others.

www.ingramcontent.com/pod-product-compliance
Lightning Source LLC
Chambersburg PA
CBHW080914170526
45158CB00008B/2107